BELOVED

This is YOUR year to create.
Make it an AMAZING year,
using your intuition and your
Tarot cards as a guide

ACKNOWLEDGEMENTS

We are so proud to share the 2021 Biddy Tarot Planner with you!

As with many of our Tarot products, the Planner is a team effort. I wish to express my deep gratitude to Tassia Assis for designing the layout of the Biddy Tarot Planner; Anthony Esselmont for designing the front cover; MJ Valentine for co-creating the New and Full Moon spreads with me and including the astrological influences for the year; Laura Hatajik for sharing the Crystal of the Month; Autumn Haile for editing the Planner and making it sparkle; Team Biddy for bringing the Planner to life; and the Biddy Tarot community for your ongoing love and support. Together, we have created something amazing, and I hope you love it!

The Tarot deck featured in the 2021 Biddy Tarot Planner is the Lumina Tarot, republished with permission from the author, Lauren Aletta from Inner Hue. The Lumina Tarot is available for sale via **www.biddytarot.com/lumina.**

Note: The exact date of lunations may vary depending on your region. This planner was made using US Pacific time. To know the exact dates for your region, go to www.timeanddate.com/moon/phases.

WELCOME

Welcome to 2021: The Year of Spiritual Awakening.

You are about to step into one of your most powerful years yet as you say YES to your intuition and your inner wisdom.

With your Tarot cards as a guide, you'll tune in to your Higher Self, manifest your goals and dreams and, most importantly, create a life that is in full alignment with your soul's purpose.

It's all possible with the Biddy Tarot Planner.

The Biddy Tarot Planner will give you the power to:

⊙ Tap into the collective energy of each month with the intuitive Tarot forecast

⊙ Use monthly rituals to deepen your connection with the collective energy

⊙ Explore the blessings of each New and Full Moon

⊙ Create personalized daily forecasts to maximize the potential of each day

⊙ Complete juicy Tarot spreads for each season and connect with what the upcoming year has in store for you

This Planner has been designed for YOU, to help you create an amazing year ahead, learn to trust your intuition and allow the Tarot cards to guide you to your most incredible year yet.

So, get out your favorite Tarot deck, grab your crystals, uncap your best markers, and prepare to get *up close and personal* with your divine power.

Lots of love and success,

B Guule

P.S.

We love celebrating our community (and that means you!) So, don't forget to share LOTS of photos and videos of your Planner on Instagram, using the hashtag **#biddytarotplanner**. And make sure you're following **@biddytarot** as we'll be sharing even more tips to help you use the Tarot to create your year of **Spiritual Awakening**.

FREE BONUS [VALUE $197]

BIDDY TAROT PLANNER TOOLKIT

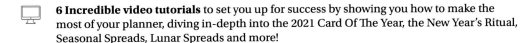

To help you achieve your highest potential and get the most out of your 2021 Biddy Tarot Planner, I've created a free bonus Toolkit, including:

6 Incredible video tutorials to set you up for success by showing you how to make the most of your planner, diving in-depth into the 2021 Card Of The Year, the New Year's Ritual, Seasonal Spreads, Lunar Spreads and more!

2 powerful meditations to help you harness the lunar universal energy regularly, including one for the New Moon and one for the Full Moon.

A guide to navigating Mercury Retrograde and a special Mercury Retrograde Tarot spread to keep you balanced and prepared for anything.

Print-your-own Tarot cards to use inside of the Planner.

4 deep-dive Tarot spreads for self-discovery, spiritual advancement, and trusting your intuition.

Detailed guidance on how to use the Daily Tarot Card practice.

And so much more!

DOWNLOAD THE FREE PLANNER KIT AT
WWW.BIDDYTAROT.COM/2021-PLANNER-BONUS

TABLE OF CONTENTS

HOW TO MAKE THE MOST OUT OF YOUR PLANNER

To get started, here's what you will need:

- ⊙ Your favorite Tarot deck
- ⊙ Your favorite markers, pens and pencils
- ⊙ Your free Bonus Planner Toolkit (download it at www.biddytarot.com/2021-planner-bonus)

If you're on Instagram, I would love to see your Tarot spreads! Use the hashtag **#biddytarotplanner** to post your photos of the Planner and your readings, and we'll share them with the Biddy Tarot community!

To create your Year of Spiritual Awakening, here's how to use your planner:

FIRST, WATCH THE VIDEO TUTORIALS...

I've created a series of tutorial videos to show you how to make the most of the Biddy Tarot Planner. I'll be there with you every step of the way!

For free access, go to www.biddytarot.com/2021-planner-bonus.

AT THE START OF THE YEAR...

Start your year with the **New Year's Ritual** (on page 16) — a divine experience of self-reflection, intuitive journaling, and Tarot card consultation.

And connect with the energy of the **2021 Tarot card — the Hierophant**. Take some time to reflect on what its energy means for you as you step into the new year.

FOR EACH SEASON...

At the start of each season, you'll be invited to do a **Seasonal Tarot Spread** to explore the energy of the season and use that energy to set your goals and intentions for the upcoming three months.

A note on location: The seasons in this Planner have been designed for those in the Northern Hemisphere. If you are in the Southern Hemisphere, please swap the seasons so you're doing the Summer Tarot Spread in December, and so on.

AT THE START OF THE MONTH...

Reflect on the **Tarot card for the month.** For each month, I've shared some initial insights — take it to the next level by connecting with what it means for you. How can you harness this energy and use it throughout the month ahead?

Next, do the **ritual** associated with the Tarot card. You may do the ritual just once during the month, or you may choose to do it more frequently. You can also continue to use the ritual in following months if you feel called to do so.

I've also recommended a **crystal** that you can work with to connect with the energy of the Tarot card. You could carry the crystal with you throughout the month, wear it, place it on your desk or in your bedroom, bring it out each time you do a Tarot reading — be creative!

Finally, I've noted the **major astrological influences** that are at play during the month so your cards and stars align.

And while we're speaking about planetary influences, keep an eye out for **Mercury Retrograde** which occurs three times this year. Mercury Retrograde is renowned for creating havoc with communication, timing, travel and technology. Avoid activities such as signing contracts, launching products, and making technical upgrades, and always double-check the details.

That said, there are also positive aspects to Mercury Retrograde — it's the perfect time for reflection, revisiting the past, reworking or closing out a project, and re-evaluating your priorities (lots of 'RE's!). For each Mercury Retrograde of the year, you can complete the Mercury Retrograde Tarot Spread (inside the *Tarot Reader's Guide to Surviving Mercury Retrograde*, in your Toolkit) to gain clarity through this potentially confusing time.

Grab it here www.biddytarot.com/2021-planner-bonus.

FOR EACH DAY...

At the beginning of each day, draw a Tarot card and set your intention for the day ahead. Note your card and thoughts in the planner. At the end of the day, reflect on what you have learned and discovered based on the energy of your daily card.

For more ideas on how to do the daily Tarot card draw, check out www.biddytarot.com/daily-tarot-card.

ON THE NEW MOON AND THE FULL MOON...

Without question, the cycles of the Moon have an impact on our own personal cycles. For each New and Full Moon, do the spread that corresponds to the astrological sign of the Moon.

Reminder: On the **New Moon**, set your intentions for the next two weeks and get ready to start new projects and make way for new beginnings. On the **Full Moon**, give thanks for what you have achieved and manifested over the past two weeks, and let go of what is no longer serving you. Don't forget to clear and cleanse your energy and your space during this time. I've created a special New Moon and Full Moon Ritual *plus* two guided visualizations so you can fully tap into the power of the lunar cycles. Access them in the Toolkit at www.biddytarot.com/2021-planner-bonus.

Note: All times and dates of the lunar cycles are in US Pacific time.

IF YOU NEED A LITTLE HELP WITH THE TAROT CARD MEANINGS...

To make the most out of the Biddy Tarot Planner, all you need is a basic knowledge of the Tarot cards and your intuition will take care of the rest! However, I know that some of you may want a little extra guidance along the way so I have two incredibly helpful resources for you:

[BOOK] THE ULTIMATE GUIDE TO TAROT CARD MEANINGS

In this modern guide to the Tarot card meanings, you'll discover how to interpret the cards in your Tarot readings with ease. An Amazon best-seller, *The Ultimate Guide to Tarot Card Meanings* includes detailed descriptions of the 78 Tarot cards, including upright and reversed meanings, and what each card means in relationship, work, finance, spiritual, and well-being readings. This is a must-have reference guide for all Tarot readers, from beginners to professionals, to help you quickly and easily decipher the meaning of your Tarot readings. Buy the book at www.biddytarot.com/guide.

MASTER THE TAROT
CARD MEANINGS

[ONLINE COURSE] MASTER THE TAROT CARD MEANINGS

My program, Master the Tarot Card Meanings, is the #1 online Tarot training course to help you instantly (and intuitively) interpret the 78 cards in the Tarot deck — without memorization.

In Master the Tarot Card Meanings, I'll show you how to build a unique personal connection with the Tarot, using simple yet powerful techniques for interpreting the cards. Plus, you'll learn the 'must know' systems that sit behind the Tarot cards to make learning Tarot super simple.

And together, we'll walk through the 78 Tarot cards, so you can master each and every one of them once and for all!

Learn more at www.biddytarot.com/mtcm or start with our free training at www.biddytarot.com/webinar-mtcm.

REMEMBER...

⊙ To make the most out of this Planner, check out my free video tutorials and bonuses at www.biddytarot.com/2021-planner-bonus.

⊙ Post photos of your Planner and Tarot spreads to Instagram with the hashtag #biddytarotplanner to get a shout-out!

WANT TO GET STARTED EARLY?

⊙ Download the Planner pages for November and December 2020 (for free!) at www.biddytarot.com/2021-planner-bonus so that you can get started straight away.

2020 REFLECTION

As we come to the end of 2020, take some time to reflect on the past 12 months and prepare yourself for the year to come.

For each question, journal your intuitive thoughts first, then if you feel called to do so, draw a Tarot card to help you go deeper.

1. What were my biggest achievements for 2020?

2. What were my biggest challenges for 2020?

3. How have I developed as a person?

4. What did I learn in 2020?

5. How would I describe 2020 in just 3 words?

6. What aspects of 2020 can I leave behind?

7. What aspects of 2020 can I bring with me into 2021?

8. What new seeds and opportunities are being planted?

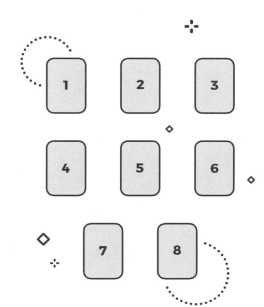

1. WHAT WERE MY BIGGEST ACHIEVEMENTS FOR 2020?

Don't forget to snap a pic of your reading and share on IG using the hashtag **#biddytarotplanner**. We love seeing you using your Biddy Tarot Planner in action and can't wait to celebrate with you!

2. WHAT WERE MY BIGGEST CHALLENGES FOR 2020?

3. HOW HAVE I DEVELOPED AS A PERSON?

4. WHAT DID I LEARN IN 2020?

5. HOW WOULD I DESCRIBE 2020 IN JUST 3 WORDS?

6. WHAT ASPECTS OF 2020 CAN I LEAVE BEHIND?

7. WHAT ASPECTS OF 2020 CAN I BRING WITH ME INTO 2021?

8. WHAT NEW SEEDS AND OPPORTUNITIES ARE BEING PLANTED?

2021

2021 THE YEAR OF THE **HIEROPHANT** AND SPIRITUAL AWAKENING

At its core, this card — and this year — is about awakening to a Higher Power, dedicating yourself to your spiritual path, and receiving guidance from wise teachers. This is a powerful year for laying the foundations of your spiritual path, and setting forth on a transformational journey that will unfold for many years to come.

Something is stirring from within — a call to a higher purpose, a desire to find deeper meaning in your life, or a more conscious way of interacting with the world around you. You know there is more to life and you are eager to discover what that truly means.

As you step into 2021, the year of the Hierophant, you have the opportunity to find your deeper meaning by learning about established belief systems, values, rituals and traditions that will support you on your path of spiritual development and fulfilment.

This is the year to make your spiritual path your priority. Dedicate yourself to a regular spiritual practice, such as daily meditation, weekly yoga, monthly circles or an annual silent retreat. This isn't just about proving you're #woke or doing the occasional 7-day challenge on Instagram. This is about a **serious dedication** to your spiritual practice. It's about making it a part of everything you do. Every day.

You'll need discipline and accountability to stay committed to your spiritual path. There will be days when it doesn't come easily to you or where you'd rather sleep in or watch TV. But true dedication to your journey means making an ongoing commitment and overcoming the challenges and obstacles along the way. Commitment is knowing that everything is part of the journey.

Seek out respected and wise teachers who nurture your spiritual awareness and help you access the Divine by understanding traditions and core principles. These teachers may appear as a coach, mentor, guru, author, spiritual

2 + 0 + 2 + 1 = 5 – HIEROPHANT

The energy of the Hierophant is represented by:

- ⊙ Dedication to your spiritual practice
- ⊙ Discipline and commitment
- ⊙ Seeking out a like-minded community

leader, friend or partner. Be open to receive their 'tried and tested' advice about what does and doesn't work. Tap into their core beliefs, as well as mindset and philosophies, as these will guide you along your personal path.

You may also undertake a period of formal spiritual study, through a class, program or online course, as you delve into a subject that has been widely explored and documented. This is your opportunity to tap into ancient wisdom and spiritual knowledge to support you in establishing your own belief systems and values.

Finally, 2021 is the year for finding your spiritual community — a group of like-minded people who share your values and who are here to support you on your path. It might be a meditation group, Full Moon circle, Tarot class, or spiritualist church. This group of people will become your safe haven for exploring your spirituality and will be your vital support system as you travel this path together.

RITUAL: DEDICATION TO YOUR SPIRITUAL PRACTICE

Light a candle, and make a dedication to your spiritual practice for 2021.

- ⊚ What do you want to learn in 2021 that will support your spiritual path?

- ⊚ Who will be your teachers and guides?

- ⊚ What spiritual practices do you commit to in your daily life?

Write the answers in your journal. Then close your eyes and make a promise to yourself to honor your spiritual development this year. Visualize yourself following your spiritual path and envision the person you will become by the end of this year. Feel the energy of this vision flow through every cell of your body. Open your eyes, then blow out the candle, saying, "And so it is."

JOURNALING PROMPTS

Use these journaling prompts throughout the year to help you stay in alignment with the Hierophant energy.

- ⊚ How can I honor my spiritual path?

- ⊚ Who can teach and guide me on my spiritual path?

- ⊚ What ancient traditions and rituals can I integrate into my everyday life?

- ⊚ What is my spiritual practice? How can I dedicate myself to it more fully?

- ⊚ What are my core values and belief systems?

Also, reflect back on 2012 — the most recent year of the Hierophant. Consider what was emerging and unfolding in your life at that time, especially on a spiritual level, and how these themes may re-emerge in 2021 and beyond.

For me, 2012 was the year I left my corporate job to dedicate my time and energy fully to Biddy Tarot. This was a pivotal year for me when I trusted in my spiritual path and took a big leap into the unknown to make spirituality a core part of my life. Now, 9 years later, Biddy Tarot has blossomed into the #1 Tarot resource online with over 9 million visitors every year (and growing).

If 2021 is to bring similar energy to 2012, then I'm excited to see what new spiritual opportunities and awakenings are to come and how they will continue to manifest and unfold as time goes on.

INSIGHTS

NEW YEAR'S RITUAL

This New Year's Ritual is a beautiful, empowering way to start the new year! You'll be connecting with your Higher Self and envisioning what you truly want to manifest in the year to come. This is about positive change and transformation at a deep, symbolic level that will help you to create an abundant, super-charged year ahead!

I encourage you to use this ritual as a guide only. Rituals become even more powerful when **you** create them, so use this as a starting point and then get creative with what you want to include.

Ready? Let's do it!

STEP 1: CREATE YOUR SACRED SPACE

Gather everything you need for the ritual and begin to create your sacred space.

Next, set up your altar. Your altar doesn't have to be super fancy. Simply use items that represent what you want to manifest in 2021. You can include crystals, Tarot cards, jewelry, flowers, rocks — whatever helps you to create a sacred intention for your ritual.

Place the candles in and around your altar. When you're all set up and ready, switch off the lights and light the candles.

Take a moment to ground yourself. Close your eyes and take in a few deep breaths. Connect in with the Earth energy and the Universal energy, feeling yourself filled with a beautiful white light.

STEP 2: REFLECT ON THE PAST YEAR

Reflect on the year that was 2020. What did you experience? What were the highs? What were the lows? And what did you learn along the way?

To support you in this process, use the New Year's Tarot Spread on page 20. Draw the first 2 cards and write your insights in the spaces provided on pages 20 and 21.

Then, write your thoughts about the past year on the next page.

BEFORE YOU START, YOU WILL NEED...

- ⊘ Your Biddy Tarot Planner

- ⊘ Your favorite Tarot deck — the Everyday Tarot Deck is a great place to start (available via www.everydaytarot.com/deck)

- ⊘ Your favorite markers

- ⊘ At least one candle and some matches

- ⊘ An herbal bundle for clearing and cleansing

- ⊘ Items for your altar. These are symbols of what you want to create in 2021, such as an image of your ideal relationship, a flower for beauty, a seed pod for starting something new — you choose!

- ⊘ At least one hour of uninterrupted time — lock the door, turn off your phone, do whatever you need to protect your sacred space

- ⊘ (Optional) Your favorite crystals — I recommend citrine for abundance and clear quartz for clarity

- ⊘ The New Year's Tarot Spread (page 20)

Remember, if you would like extra guidance for the New Year's Ritual, watch the free video tutorials at www.biddytarot.com/2021-planner-bonus

INSIGHTS

Take the herbal bundle and light it. Then, wave the smoke around your body, front and back, as you cleanse your aura and release any old energy that may be clinging to you. For each item on your list, say aloud, "I release myself of... {insert what you want to release}."

When you feel complete, say aloud three times, **"I give thanks for the past year. I release what no longer serves me. And I welcome new opportunities with open arms."**

Now, close your eyes and start to imagine what you want to create in 2021.

Think about what you want to create in your relationships. Imagine it as if it were a movie in your mind, experiencing everything you want to experience in your relationships for 2021. See yourself being an active participant in the movie. See what you see. Hear what you hear. Feel what you feel. Taste what you taste. And smell what you smell. Create a full sensory experience.

When you're ready, wipe the movie screen clean, and bring up a new movie, this time about your career, work and finances. What do you want to create in your material world? Create a full sensory experience.

When you're complete, bring up the next movie for your health and well-being. And after that, your personal development. What do you want to create?

When you feel complete, open your eyes, and write down your experiences on the next page.

Next, take out your Tarot cards and continue with Cards 3 to 9 of the New Year's Tarot Spread. Write your cards and insights in the space provided on pages 21 to 23.

RELATIONSHIPS

HEALTH AND WELL-BEING

CAREER AND FINANCES

PERSONAL DEVELOPMENT

STEP 4: MANIFEST YOUR GOALS FOR 2021

Read over your insights from Step 3 and choose 10 things you want to manifest in 2021 (e.g. I want to be fit and healthy, or I want to take a 3-month vacation).

Then, change these to "I am" statements (yes, even if they sound a little funny). For example, "I AM fit and healthy" or "I AM enjoying a 3-month vacation." Take a moment to feel the energy and the vibration of these "I am" statements — super powerful, right?!

Now, complete your New Year Tarot Spread from Cards 10 to 12 and write your cards and insights in the spaces provided on pages 23 and 24.

Finally, close your eyes and visualize the energy of what you want to create as a bright white light. Imagine it as a ball of light radiating within your solar plexus (just above your belly button). Then imagine the ball of light getting bigger and bigger, filling your body, flowing through your aura, and illuminating out into the world. This is your power, your determination, your ability to manifest your goals, just as you see them. And so it is done. When you are ready, gently open your eyes.

STEP 5: CLOSE THE SPACE

Before you close the space, check in with your Higher Self and ask if there is anything else that needs to be done before this ritual is complete. Sometimes your intuition may guide you towards another sacred activity before you know for sure that you are done.

When you're ready, say a prayer of thanks to your Higher Self for guiding you along this process. Then, say out loud, "And so it is."

Blow out the candles, turn on the lights, then pack up the space. You may wish to leave part of your altar there or move it somewhere more convenient, so you have a visual reminder of this beautiful ritual that you have gifted yourself.

INSIGHTS

NEW YEAR'S TAROT SPREAD

Gain the clarity you need for your Year of Spiritual Awakening with the New Year's Tarot Spread. This is a powerful spread to use at the start of the year. Or, use it on your birthday to gain valuable insight into what you might experience during your next year of life.

1. The previous year in summary

2. Lessons learned from the past year

3. Aspirations for the next 12 months

4. What empowers you in reaching your aspirations

5. What may stand in the way of reaching your aspirations

6. Your relationships and emotions in the coming year

7. Your career, work and finances

8. Your health and well-being

9. Your spiritual energy and inner fulfilment

10. What you most need to focus on in the year ahead

11. Your most important lesson for the coming year

12. Overall, where are you headed in the next 12 months

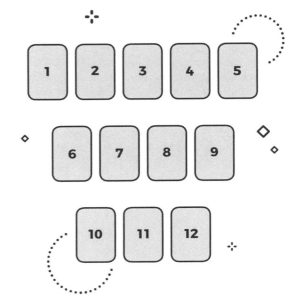

1. THE PREVIOUS YEAR IN SUMMARY

Excited with what 2021 might bring you? Post a pic of your spread using the hashtag
#biddytarotplanner and we'll share with the Biddy Tarot community!

2. LESSONS LEARNED FROM THE PAST YEAR

3. ASPIRATIONS FOR THE NEXT 12 MONTHS

4. WHAT EMPOWERS YOU IN REACHING YOUR ASPIRATIONS

5. WHAT MAY STAND IN THE WAY OF REACHING YOUR ASPIRATIONS

6. YOUR RELATIONSHIPS AND EMOTIONS IN THE COMING YEAR

7. YOUR CAREER, WORK AND FINANCES

8. YOUR HEALTH AND WELL-BEING

9. YOUR SPIRITUAL ENERGY AND INNER FULFILMENT

10. WHAT YOU MOST NEED TO FOCUS ON IN THE YEAR AHEAD

11. YOUR MOST IMPORTANT LESSON FOR THE COMING YEAR

12. OVERALL, WHERE ARE YOU HEADED IN THE NEXT 12 MONTHS

JANUARY

THE STAR

With the sparkling energy of the Star card in January, you are leaving behind what has been a challenging and unpredictable 2020, and starting the new year with a renewed sense of hope and faith. You can trust that life *can* and *will* be different. You are ready to transform from the old you to the new you and, in doing so, you're choosing to live in alignment with the highest version of yourself. As you step into 2021, allow yourself to dream, to aspire, to elevate in any way possible, so that you can truly reach the stars. They are right here waiting for you.

 ### RITUAL: CLEANSING AND RENEWAL

First, prepare to cleanse yourself in a body of water. This can be a relaxing salt bath or a peaceful dip in the ocean. Whatever you choose. As you immerse yourself in the water, say to yourself, "I wash away 2020" and feel all the energy of the previous year wash away in the ebb and flow. Experience the buoyant release of the water and sense of renewal and rejuvenation. Next, it's time to reflect. After your cleansing, grab your journal and write your messages of hope for 2021. Start by writing, "In 2021, I wish for..." then pour out all your dreams and hopes for the year ahead in the journal.

 ### CRYSTAL: CLEAR QUARTZ

Clear Quartz is the perfect stone to support you in gaining the clarity you need to go within and focus on exactly what you wish for. Even better, find a quartz that has a rainbow inclusion — it will inspire you to realize what it is you need in order to be the best possible version of yourself!

 ### ASTROLOGICAL INFLUENCES

January 9 | Venus trine Mars: This aspect between Venus and Mars brings ease to your interactions. Mars gives your social and romantic life a lively, dynamic edge. New partnerships formed now may be fruitful.

January 19 | Aquarius season begins:
Idealism, individualism, originality, spontaneity, independence.

January 30–February 20 | Mercury Retrograde in Aquarius:
Utilize the Tarot Reader's Guide for Mercury Retrograde inside of your Toolkit at www.biddytarot.com/2021-planner-bonus to help navigate through this time.

INSIGHTS

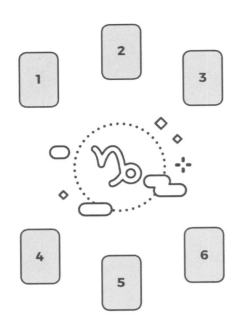

JANUARY 12
NEW MOON IN CAPRICORN

The first New Moon of the year falls in Capricorn, which rules stability, structure and goals. It's a great time to work on a solid plan that will bring your dreams to life in the new year.

1. What insights did I gain in 2020 around what I want to achieve in 2021?

2. Which areas of my life might benefit from creating a sense of order?

3. How can I best support my financial goals this year?

4. What goals do I want to achieve within the next six months?

5. What kind of structure do I need to establish to support those goals?

6. Which grounding practices would best support me this year?

INSIGHTS

1. nine of cups - I open my grateful heart to the gifts that are coming my way. What you have been working toward is coming to you, so enjoy life's pleasures and sink into awe and wonder of a joyous heart

2. two of pentacles - I create an equilibrium in my life that allows me to be my best self. be patient, flexible, and adaptable as you try to juggle your responsibilities with your family, friends, work, finances, health, and new challenges. time - management

3. five of wands - I support others and they support me, and we rise together in accelerated harmony. I heard the word: accountability. you need a constructive environment where you can test your ideas and have them challenged (and improved) by others.

4. ace of pentacles - I plant my goals with intention, direct focus, and faith. a new financial or career opportunity, manifestation, abundance. see the ace of pentacles as your green light. it marks the initial stages of manifesting your goals and assures you that you can truly achieve what you have set your mind do

5. page of swords - I learn and I expand my consciousness, and open up new opportunities for my life. remain open to unexpected lessons, share truthfully, and delight in every interaction. curiosity, thirst for knowledge - be open to new ways of expressing yourself and discovering where your inner talents lie

6. the emperor - I lead the circumstances in my world with confidence, harmony, and generosity - address any issues you harbor around authority, control, and willpower. remain flexible and keenly aware of your own energetic boundaries and motives. embody confident, compassionate leadership and exercise sovereignty over your own reality.

We love seeing you use your Biddy Tarot Planner! Completed this spread? Make sure you post a pic on Instagram and be sure to use the hashtag #biddytarotplanner so we can celebrate with you!

JANUARY 28

FULL MOON IN LEO

Feel into the fullness of creativity and play, and get ready to shine with the Leo Full Moon. Celebrate your unique warmth and brilliance bathed in this wonderful energy.

1. What am I most proud of having achieved in the last six months?

2. How has my past courage impacted my personal growth?

3. What are some limiting beliefs I hold about myself?

4. What new stories can I tell myself instead?

5. Where in my life might I need to be more humble?

6. How could I express myself more authentically this year?

INSIGHTS

JAN 01 FRIDAY   CARD OF THE DAY:

▷ INTENTION   ▷ REFLECTION

JAN 02 SATURDAY   CARD OF THE DAY:

▷ INTENTION   ▷ REFLECTION

JAN 03 SUNDAY   CARD OF THE DAY:

▷ INTENTION   ▷ REFLECTION

JAN 04 MONDAY   CARD OF THE DAY:

▷ INTENTION   ▷ REFLECTION

JAN 05 TUESDAY   CARD OF THE DAY:

▷ INTENTION   ▷ REFLECTION

JAN 06 WEDNESDAY   CARD OF THE DAY:

▷ INTENTION   ▷ REFLECTION

JAN 07 THURSDAY   CARD OF THE DAY:

▷ INTENTION   ▷ REFLECTION

JAN 08 FRIDAY

CARD OF THE DAY:

▷ INTENTION

▷ REFLECTION

JAN 09 SATURDAY | *Venus trine Mars*

CARD OF THE DAY:

▷ INTENTION

▷ REFLECTION

JAN 10 SUNDAY

CARD OF THE DAY:

▷ INTENTION

▷ REFLECTION

JAN 11 MONDAY

CARD OF THE DAY: the tower

▷ INTENTION In chaos, I move toward the brightest light.

▷ REFLECTION a tower moment hits and throws you for a loop. a lightning bolt of clarity and insight cuts through the lies and illusions you have been telling yourself, and now the truth comes to light

JAN 12 TUESDAY | ◌ *New Moon in Capricorn*

CARD OF THE DAY: seven of wands

▷ INTENTION I am deserving of this success and I will bravely shine my light into the world.

▷ REFLECTION remain synchronized and aligned with your bright vision and reject any low vibe, negative states that others may be pushing

JAN 13 WEDNESDAY

CARD OF THE DAY:

▷ INTENTION

▷ REFLECTION

JAN 14 THURSDAY

CARD OF THE DAY:

▷ INTENTION

▷ REFLECTION

JAN 15 FRIDAY

CARD OF THE DAY:

▷ INTENTION

▷ REFLECTION

JAN 16 SATURDAY

CARD OF THE DAY: Knight of swords

▷ INTENTION

I move quickly to help others and, as I do, my dream expands
ambition. action. driven. quick-thinking

▷ REFLECTION

Strive for excellence every single day in order to bring a little of his magic into your life

don't RUSH to settle down!

JAN 17 SUNDAY

CARD OF THE DAY: queen of pentacles

▷ INTENTION I enjoy my deeply connected life and I lead it with an outpouring of warmth, abundance, and love. you are embodying the ultimate working parent archetype. it is important to you to live independently, with a stable income and with enough time/space to nurture your loved ones

▷ REFLECTION you are safe. this a positive message of creature comforts and happiness, and this earthly medicine ushers in a life well lived in the material world.

don't overextend your energy, avoid enabling others by overmothering them

JAN 18 MONDAY

CARD OF THE DAY:

▷ INTENTION

▷ REFLECTION

JAN 19 TUESDAY | *Aquarius season begins*

CARD OF THE DAY:

▷ INTENTION

▷ REFLECTION

JAN 20 WEDNESDAY

CARD OF THE DAY:

▷ INTENTION

▷ REFLECTION

JAN 21 THURSDAY

CARD OF THE DAY:

▷ INTENTION

▷ REFLECTION

JAN 22 FRIDAY

CARD OF THE DAY:

▷ INTENTION

▷ REFLECTION

JAN 23 SATURDAY

CARD OF THE DAY:

▷ INTENTION

▷ REFLECTION

JAN 24 SUNDAY

CARD OF THE DAY:

▷ INTENTION

▷ REFLECTION

JAN 25 MONDAY

CARD OF THE DAY:

▷ INTENTION

▷ REFLECTION

JAN 26 TUESDAY

CARD OF THE DAY:

▷ INTENTION

▷ REFLECTION

JAN 27 WEDNESDAY

CARD OF THE DAY:

▷ INTENTION

▷ REFLECTION

JAN 28 THURSDAY | ● *Full Moon in Leo*

CARD OF THE DAY:

▷ INTENTION

▷ REFLECTION

JAN 29 FRIDAY

CARD OF THE DAY:

▷ INTENTION

▷ REFLECTION

JAN 30 SATURDAY | *Mercury Retrograde begins*

CARD OF THE DAY:

▷ INTENTION

▷ REFLECTION

JAN 31 SUNDAY

CARD OF THE DAY:

▷ INTENTION

▷ REFLECTION

INSIGHTS

FEBRUARY

THE WORLD

In February, you are becoming more consciously aware of your role in the global community, and how you can change and influence the world on a deeper level. You are not simply operating from a place of selfish need, but you're beginning to consider the greater whole and seeking out solutions that serve the highest good.

On a personal level, you are coming into wholeness, discovering how to integrate all the different facets of yourself so you can show up as your most authentic and aligned self. You are no longer holding back or denying any part of who you are. Instead, you accept yourself completely and are ready to radiate your light into the world.

RITUAL: WHO AM I?

It's time for some self-reflection. Ask yourself, "Who am I?" What are your different roles, identities, or aspects of your personality? Spill your responses onto the page of your journal continuously for at least 10 minutes. Then, close your eyes and visualize fully expressing all these parts of yourself in a way that feels 'whole' and true to you. Ask yourself, "How can I serve the community, in this state of wholeness?" Lastly, write your responses in your journal.

CRYSTAL: AMETHYST

A high-vibrational and protective stone, Amethyst balances out the highs and lows of life, bringing peace and understanding. It helps you to remain focused and appreciative of all the blessings around you.

ASTROLOGICAL INFLUENCES

February 1 | Venus into Aquarius: Venus dances into Aquarius, bringing independence to our romantic and social lives. This transit encourages experimentation. Use this opportunity to express yourself more freely.

February 13 | Mars sextile Neptune: This influence takes sensuality and romance to new heights! Your romantic desires may deepen, creating alluring magnetism and karmic connections. This is also a time to fight passionately for a good cause.

February 20 | Pisces season begins:
Emotion, awareness, artistry, spirituality, intuition.

INSIGHTS

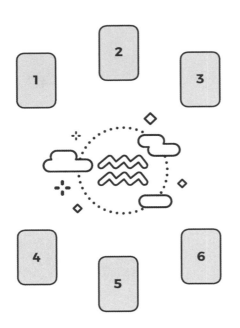

NEW MOON IN AQUARIUS

An Aquarius New Moon is an opportunity to set out-of-the-box intentions — make your plans according to what you really want, not what other people think or expect.

1. What unique gifts do I bring to the table?

2. How can I best utilize these gifts for the betterment of humanity?

3. Where would I most like to see social change and equality?

4. How am I best-placed to communicate my ideas with the world?

5. How can I connect with others who align with my vision for the future?

6. Which areas of my life would benefit from expressing vulnerability?

INSIGHTS

FULL MOON IN VIRGO

Honor the ways you are serving the world and the places you are creating order from chaos at this Virgo Full Moon.

1. What can I offer to my family and friends to be of the highest service?

2. Which areas of my life might benefit from creating order?

3. How might I benefit from working hard in the next six months?

4. How can I limit clutter in my physical space?

5. What can I do to better support my mental clarity?

6. How can I best support healthy emotional expression?

INSIGHTS

On Instagram? Post a photo of your spread and your Tarot Planner with the hashtag **#biddytarotplanner** and we'll share with the Biddy Tarot community!

FEBRUARY | 35

FEB 01   MONDAY | *Venus into Aquarius*   CARD OF THE DAY:

▷ INTENTION   ▷ REFLECTION

FEB 02   TUESDAY   CARD OF THE DAY:

▷ INTENTION   ▷ REFLECTION

FEB 03   WEDNESDAY   CARD OF THE DAY:

▷ INTENTION   ▷ REFLECTION

FEB 04   THURSDAY   CARD OF THE DAY:

▷ INTENTION   ▷ REFLECTION

FEB 05   FRIDAY   CARD OF THE DAY:

▷ INTENTION   ▷ REFLECTION

FEB 06   SATURDAY   CARD OF THE DAY:

▷ INTENTION   ▷ REFLECTION

FEB 07   SUNDAY   CARD OF THE DAY:

▷ INTENTION   ▷ REFLECTION

FEB 08   MONDAY

CARD OF THE DAY:

▷ INTENTION

▷ REFLECTION

FEB 09   TUESDAY

CARD OF THE DAY:

▷ INTENTION

▷ REFLECTION

FEB 10   WEDNESDAY

CARD OF THE DAY:

▷ INTENTION

▷ REFLECTION

FEB 11   THURSDAY | *New Moon in Aquarius*

CARD OF THE DAY:

▷ INTENTION

▷ REFLECTION

FEB 12   FRIDAY

CARD OF THE DAY:

▷ INTENTION

▷ REFLECTION

FEB 13   SATURDAY | *Mars sextile Neptune*

CARD OF THE DAY:

▷ INTENTION

▷ REFLECTION

FEB 14   SUNDAY

CARD OF THE DAY:

▷ INTENTION

▷ REFLECTION

FEB 15   MONDAY   CARD OF THE DAY:

▷ INTENTION   ▷ REFLECTION

FEB 16   TUESDAY   CARD OF THE DAY:

▷ INTENTION   ▷ REFLECTION

FEB 17   WEDNESDAY   CARD OF THE DAY:

▷ INTENTION   ▷ REFLECTION

FEB 18   THURSDAY   CARD OF THE DAY:

▷ INTENTION   ▷ REFLECTION

FEB 19   FRIDAY   CARD OF THE DAY:

▷ INTENTION   ▷ REFLECTION

FEB 20   SATURDAY | *Mercury Retrograde ends*   CARD OF THE DAY:
                                 Pisces season begins

▷ INTENTION   ▷ REFLECTION

FEB 21   SUNDAY   CARD OF THE DAY:

▷ INTENTION   ▷ REFLECTION

FEB 22 MONDAY   CARD OF THE DAY:

▷ INTENTION   ▷ REFLECTION

FEB 23 TUESDAY   CARD OF THE DAY:

▷ INTENTION   ▷ REFLECTION

FEB 24 WEDNESDAY   CARD OF THE DAY:

▷ INTENTION   ▷ REFLECTION

FEB 25 THURSDAY   CARD OF THE DAY:

▷ INTENTION   ▷ REFLECTION

FEB 26 FRIDAY   CARD OF THE DAY:

▷ INTENTION   ▷ REFLECTION

FEB 27 SATURDAY | ● *Full Moon in Virgo*   CARD OF THE DAY:

▷ INTENTION   ▷ REFLECTION

FEB 28 SUNDAY   CARD OF THE DAY:

▷ INTENTION   ▷ REFLECTION

MARCH

THE HIGH PRIESTESS

THE HIGH PRIESTESS

The High Priestess in March is an invitation to create alignment between your inner and outer worlds. Explore your inner world through meditation, journaling, reading Tarot or spending time in nature. Don't forget to listen attentively to the voice of your inner wisdom. What messages and advice does she have for you? Are you listening to her intuitive nudges? And how can you bring this inner wisdom into your outer world? You have the opportunity to live a multi-dimensional, highly conscious life if you can tune into your intuition and make it a part of your everyday life. Now is the time to make choices that are in alignment with your Higher Self.

RITUAL: DAILY TUNING IN

You'll need an amethyst and labradorite crystal for this ritual (or your favorite crystals for intuition). Lay down on your back and place the amethyst on your third eye chakra (between your brows) and the labradorite on your heart chakra (in the center of your chest). As you inhale, visualize white light flowing into an illuminating indigo ball in the center of your third eye chakra. As you exhale, visualize the light radiating, softening and growing bigger. When you feel connected, ask yourself, "What does my Highest Self want me to know right now?" Continue to breathe into your third eye chakra and invite your inner wisdom to speak to you. When you feel ready, sit up and write down the messages that came through for you.

CRYSTAL: LABRADORITE

Labradorite awakens you to your inner consciousness, taking you deep within to access your Higher Self, your inner being and your source of all wisdom. It is a powerful stone that aids in intuition, psychic abilities, clairvoyance and a deeper connection to one's true self.

⊘ ASTROLOGICAL INFLUENCES

March 3 | Mercury square Mars: Take a few deep breaths before retaliating — people are more irritable than usual, so don't take it personally. Avoid scheduling meetings and making hasty decisions at work.

March 15 | Mercury into Pisces: This transit brings a practical dimension to our dreams and spirituality. Allow your imagination to inspire ideas and communication. Create or update a vision board, or put ideas down on paper. Intuition is your best asset now.

March 21 | Aries season begins:
Passion, motivation, confidence, tact, excitement.

INSIGHTS

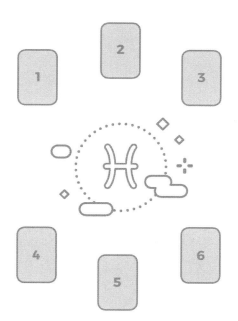

NEW MOON IN PISCES

Now is the time to let your imagination run wild and dream big. Tap into your intuition and set intentions to bring your visions to life.

1. How can I connect more deeply with my intuition?

2. What can I do to bring myself into alignment with the highest good?

3. What am I currently manifesting in my life?

4. How can I align my emotions to support positive manifestations?

5. What new creative projects am I called to begin now?

6. How can I further develop my spiritual practice?

INSIGHTS

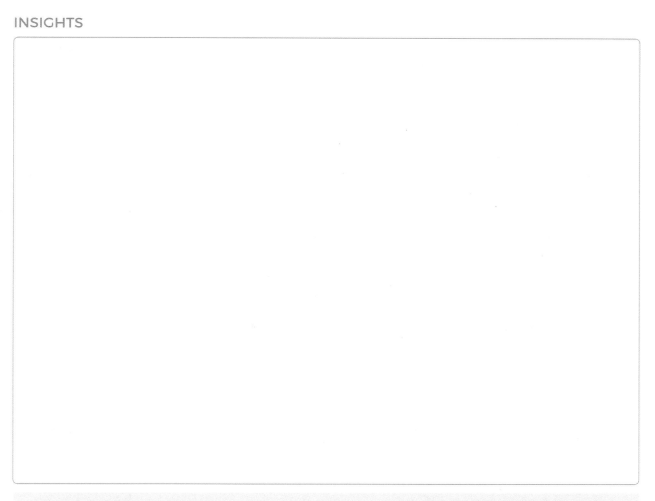

Don't forget to snap a pic of your reading and share on IG using the hashtag **#biddytarotplanner**. We love seeing you using your Biddy Tarot Planner in action and can't wait to celebrate with you!

MARCH 28
FULL MOON IN LIBRA

The Libra Full Moon invites you to revel in beauty and release the things that negatively impact your sense of harmony and balance.

1. What support might I benefit from to help me make the best choices?

2. What can I do to create more balance in my closest relationships?

3. Where is the greatest imbalance in my life right now?

4. What do I need to release in order to be more objective moving forward?

5. What do I need to do to feel more steadfast in my decision-making?

6. How can I manifest more beauty in my life?

INSIGHTS

MAR 01 MONDAY

CARD OF THE DAY:

▷ INTENTION

▷ REFLECTION

MAR 02 TUESDAY

CARD OF THE DAY:

▷ INTENTION

▷ REFLECTION

MAR 03 WEDNESDAY | *Mercury square Mars*

CARD OF THE DAY:

▷ INTENTION

▷ REFLECTION

MAR 04 THURSDAY

CARD OF THE DAY:

▷ INTENTION

▷ REFLECTION

MAR 05 FRIDAY

CARD OF THE DAY:

▷ INTENTION

▷ REFLECTION

MAR 06 SATURDAY

CARD OF THE DAY:

▷ INTENTION

▷ REFLECTION

MAR 07 SUNDAY

CARD OF THE DAY:

▷ INTENTION

▷ REFLECTION

MAR 08 MONDAY

CARD OF THE DAY: the Hierophant

▷ INTENTION I am my own guru, and the guidance i need is rooted in my faith, my belief, and my unique essence

▷ REFLECTION be open to new paradigms, perspectives, and teachers in your life look to the patterns around you and strive to understand your own internal compass

MAR 09 TUESDAY

CARD OF THE DAY:

▷ INTENTION

▷ REFLECTION

MAR 10 WEDNESDAY

CARD OF THE DAY:

▷ INTENTION

▷ REFLECTION

MAR 11 THURSDAY

CARD OF THE DAY:

▷ INTENTION

▷ REFLECTION

MAR 12 FRIDAY

CARD OF THE DAY:

▷ INTENTION

▷ REFLECTION

MAR 13 SATURDAY | ○ New Moon in Pisces

CARD OF THE DAY:

▷ INTENTION

▷ REFLECTION

MAR 14 SUNDAY

CARD OF THE DAY:

▷ INTENTION

▷ REFLECTION

MAR 15 MONDAY | *Mercury into Pisces*   CARD OF THE DAY:

▷ INTENTION   ▷ REFLECTION

MAR 16 TUESDAY   CARD OF THE DAY:

▷ INTENTION   ▷ REFLECTION

MAR 17 WEDNESDAY   CARD OF THE DAY:

▷ INTENTION   ▷ REFLECTION

MAR 18 THURSDAY   CARD OF THE DAY:

▷ INTENTION   ▷ REFLECTION

MAR 19 FRIDAY   CARD OF THE DAY:

▷ INTENTION   ▷ REFLECTION

MAR 20 SATURDAY   CARD OF THE DAY:

▷ INTENTION   ▷ REFLECTION

MAR 21 SUNDAY | *Aries season begins*   CARD OF THE DAY:

▷ INTENTION   ▷ REFLECTION

MAR 22 MONDAY   CARD OF THE DAY:

▷ INTENTION   ▷ REFLECTION

MAR 23 TUESDAY   CARD OF THE DAY:

▷ INTENTION   ▷ REFLECTION

MAR 24 WEDNESDAY   CARD OF THE DAY:

▷ INTENTION   ▷ REFLECTION

MAR 25 THURSDAY   CARD OF THE DAY:

▷ INTENTION   ▷ REFLECTION

MAR 26 FRIDAY   CARD OF THE DAY:

▷ INTENTION   ▷ REFLECTION

MAR 27 SATURDAY   CARD OF THE DAY:

▷ INTENTION   ▷ REFLECTION

MAR 28 SUNDAY | ● *Full Moon in Libra*   CARD OF THE DAY:

▷ INTENTION   ▷ REFLECTION

MAR 29 MONDAY

CARD OF THE DAY:

▷ INTENTION

▷ REFLECTION

MAR 30 TUESDAY

CARD OF THE DAY:

▷ INTENTION

▷ REFLECTION

MAR 31 WEDNESDAY

CARD OF THE DAY:

▷ INTENTION

▷ REFLECTION

INSIGHTS

SPRING EQUINOX SPREAD

Spring Equinox (March 20, 9:37 am UTC in the Northern Hemisphere; September 22, 7:21 pm UTC in the Southern Hemisphere) honors new growth and opportunity. The seeds have been planted and, nurtured by the rain, they are now emerging from the earth into the brightness of the sunlight, blossoming into beautiful flowers, fruit and foliage. Springtime is filled with color, scents and a feeling of excitement and anticipation of what's to come.

This is the perfect time to explore new possibilities, start new projects, and truly bloom under the rays of this positive light. Use the following Tarot spread around the time of the Spring Equinox to connect with this sacred energy.

1. What has emerged for me over the Winter period?

2. What lessons have I learned?

3. What new seeds are beginning to sprout?

4. How can I nurture these new opportunities?

5. How am I truly blossoming?

6. How can I best embrace the Spring energy?

INSIGHTS

INSIGHTS

SPRING EQUINOX INTENTIONS

Holding the energy and insight of your Spring Equinox Tarot Reading, set your intentions for the next three months:

APRIL

WHEEL OF FORTUNE

Take a wild guess about what's going to unfold this month, because truth be told, you have no idea! With the Wheel of Fortune energy influencing April, expect the unexpected. You may undergo massive highs but also massive lows — "what goes up must come down." You will discover the cyclical nature of life this month by appreciating those moments when everything feels perfect and aligned as well as those moments when you feel deeply challenged yet knowing that these experiences are making you stronger. Let go of the need to control the outcome and go with the flow. Enjoy the ride!

 ### RITUAL: HONORING YOUR LIFE CYCLES

In your journal, draw a timeline through the middle of the page, starting with when you were born to your current age. Then, map out your biggest life events, with the most positive experiences above the line, and the most challenging or negative experiences below the line. For example, being born into a loving family might be a 'high' but being bullied in high school might be a 'low.' Draw a line between each life event, and notice how life flows from highs to lows to highs again — a cyclical timeline you continue to thrive on. Then, find the Wheel of Fortune card in your favorite deck and place it in front of you. Reflect on the card and the role that cycles play in your life. How have you been able to adapt and adjust to them? Write down your insights in your journal, and return to them any time you need some words of encouragement.

 ### CRYSTAL: GREEN AVENTURINE

To support the ritual, include a piece of Green Aventurine. It carries a deep connection to the Earth and helps to provide a vibration of soothing appreciation for all of life's blessings. Additionally, it is known as the "Stone of Opportunity" and is one of the luckiest stones, which makes it a must-have for continuing your good fortunes.

 ### ASTROLOGICAL INFLUENCES

April 3 | Mercury into Aries: Aries encourages Mercury to make snap decisions. 'Pros and cons' lists will be helpful during this transit. Assert your point of view — but give others a chance to do the same.

April 16 | Mars trine Jupiter: Jupiter partners with Mars today, giving you the edge in competition and success. If you have a goal, a project, or even a relationship you've been avoiding, take action. Go boldly.

April 20 | Taurus season begins:
Stability, reliability, affection, sensuality, indulgence.

INSIGHTS

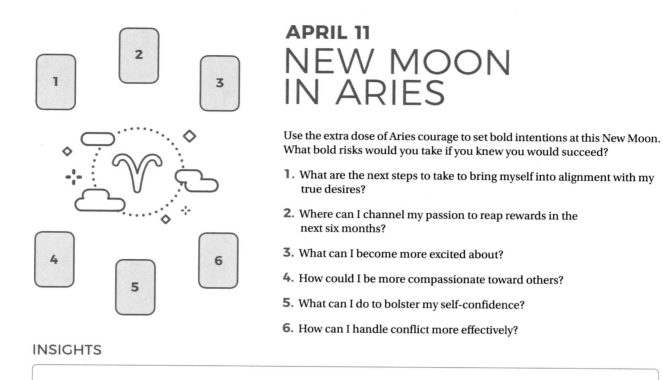

NEW MOON IN ARIES

Use the extra dose of Aries courage to set bold intentions at this New Moon. What bold risks would you take if you knew you would succeed?

1. What are the next steps to take to bring myself into alignment with my true desires?

2. Where can I channel my passion to reap rewards in the next six months?

3. What can I become more excited about?

4. How could I be more compassionate toward others?

5. What can I do to bolster my self-confidence?

6. How can I handle conflict more effectively?

INSIGHTS

We love seeing you use your Biddy Tarot Planner! Completed this spread? Make sure you post a pic on Instagram and be sure to use the hashtag **#biddytarotplanner** so we can celebrate with you!

FULL MOON IN SCORPIO

Intense energies surround the Scorpio Full Moon, creating an ideal time for shadow work and transformational activities. Use this energy to release anything that no longer resonates with your true self.

1. What feelings have I been avoiding?

2. What lessons have I learned through trying times in the past six months?

3. What intense emotions are coming up for me now?

4. How can I express my emotions more healthily?

5. What do I need to release in order to experience deep transformation?

6. Where do I need to relinquish control in my life?

INSIGHTS

APR 01 THURSDAY

CARD OF THE DAY:

▷ INTENTION

▷ REFLECTION

APR 02 FRIDAY

CARD OF THE DAY:

▷ INTENTION

▷ REFLECTION

APR 03 SATURDAY | *Mercury into Aries*

CARD OF THE DAY:

▷ INTENTION

▷ REFLECTION

APR 04 SUNDAY

CARD OF THE DAY:

▷ INTENTION

▷ REFLECTION

APR 05 MONDAY

CARD OF THE DAY:

▷ INTENTION

▷ REFLECTION

APR 06 TUESDAY

CARD OF THE DAY:

▷ INTENTION

▷ REFLECTION

APR 07 WEDNESDAY

CARD OF THE DAY:

▷ INTENTION

▷ REFLECTION

APR 08 THURSDAY

CARD OF THE DAY:

▷ INTENTION

▷ REFLECTION

APR 09 FRIDAY

CARD OF THE DAY:

▷ INTENTION

▷ REFLECTION

APR 10 SATURDAY

CARD OF THE DAY:

▷ INTENTION

▷ REFLECTION

APR 11 SUNDAY | ○ *New Moon in Aries*

CARD OF THE DAY:

▷ INTENTION

▷ REFLECTION

APR 12 MONDAY

CARD OF THE DAY:

▷ INTENTION

▷ REFLECTION

APR 13 TUESDAY

CARD OF THE DAY:

▷ INTENTION

▷ REFLECTION

APR 14 WEDNESDAY

CARD OF THE DAY:

▷ INTENTION

▷ REFLECTION

APR 15   THURSDAY   CARD OF THE DAY:

▷ INTENTION   ▷ REFLECTION

APR 16   FRIDAY | *Mars trine Jupiter*   CARD OF THE DAY:

▷ INTENTION   ▷ REFLECTION

APR 17   SATURDAY   CARD OF THE DAY:

▷ INTENTION   ▷ REFLECTION

APR 18   SUNDAY   CARD OF THE DAY:

▷ INTENTION   ▷ REFLECTION

APR 19   MONDAY   CARD OF THE DAY:

▷ INTENTION   ▷ REFLECTION

APR 20   TUESDAY | *Taurus season begins*   CARD OF THE DAY:

▷ INTENTION   ▷ REFLECTION

APR 21   WEDNESDAY   CARD OF THE DAY:

▷ INTENTION   ▷ REFLECTION

APR 22   THURSDAY   CARD OF THE DAY:

▷ INTENTION   ▷ REFLECTION

APR 23   FRIDAY   CARD OF THE DAY:

▷ INTENTION   ▷ REFLECTION

APR 24   SATURDAY   CARD OF THE DAY:

▷ INTENTION   ▷ REFLECTION

APR 25   SUNDAY   CARD OF THE DAY:

▷ INTENTION   ▷ REFLECTION

APR 26   MONDAY | ● *Full Moon in Scorpio*   CARD OF THE DAY:

▷ INTENTION   ▷ REFLECTION

APR 27   TUESDAY   CARD OF THE DAY:

▷ INTENTION   ▷ REFLECTION

APR 28   WEDNESDAY   CARD OF THE DAY:

▷ INTENTION   ▷ REFLECTION

APR 29 THURSDAY   CARD OF THE DAY:

▷ INTENTION   ▷ REFLECTION

APR 30 FRIDAY   CARD OF THE DAY:

▷ INTENTION   ▷ REFLECTION

INSIGHTS

MAY

THE FOOL

May is the month of new beginnings, wild abandonment, and throwing caution to the wind. The Fool encourages you to live life to the fullest and see the world through completely new eyes. This month, notice the little things that you've never stopped to notice before. Take joy in the gifts that the world has to offer you right now. This is also the time for you to take a leap of faith and step into the unknown, knowing that it could bring you new experiences and amazing opportunities beyond what you could have ever imagined. Be fun and spontaneous. Forget your routine and schedule this month — be free!

RITUAL: NEVER HAVE I EVER

Write a list of things you've never tried before. Include things like activities you've never attempted, food you haven't tried, or places you've never visited. If it comes to your mind, write it down. Each week, pick three things from your list and do them! For example, in our family we have Magical Mystery Tours. We randomly pick a nearby suburb, and spend the whole day there, trying out new cafes, parks, walks, and museums (even if it's the local volunteer history museum). You won't always find these on TripAdvisor, but it makes for a fun day of exploration.

CRYSTAL: DALMATIAN STONE

The Dalmatian Stone helps you to tune into your inner-child and stimulate a sense of playfulness and fun. It will help you to get out of your head and into your body to fully experience the world around you.

✦ ASTROLOGICAL INFLUENCES

May 6 | Venus trine Pluto: Pluto empowers Venus, bringing focus and confidence in relationships. Seize an opportunity in love or finances. Be open to discovering something new about your romantic nature.

May 21 | Gemini season begins:
Communication, impulsiveness, logic, enthusiasm, light-heartedness.

May 29–June 22 | Mercury Retrograde in Gemini: Utilize the Tarot Reader's Guide for Mercury Retrograde inside of your Toolkit at www.biddytarot.com/2021-planner-bonus to help navigate through this time.

INSIGHTS

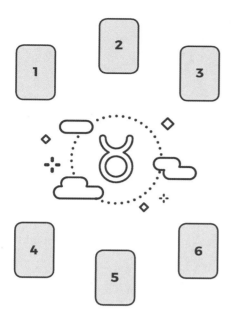

MAY 11

NEW MOON IN TAURUS

With the New Moon in Taurus, you have the chance to become conscious about creating peaceful and pleasurable experiences in your life. Use this energy to develop empowering new habits.

1. What can I do to inspire tranquility in my home?

2. What lessons can I learn from nature?

3. How can I release unhealthy attachments to physical possessions?

4. What simple pleasures would I most enjoy right now?

5. What activities will help me become more grounded in my physical self?

6. What can I do to manage overindulgence?

INSIGHTS

MAY 26
FULL MOON
IN SAGITTARIUS

Ideals and visions are heightened with this Full Moon in Sagittarius. Tap into this expansive energy and release anything that is keeping you small.

1. Where do I need to focus on expanding my awareness?

2. What do I need to release in order to achieve my goals?

3. What is my ideal vision for the global community?

4. How might short- or long-term travel benefit me in the next six months?

5. What can I do to connect more deeply with my friends?

6. What do I need to let go of in order to truly inspire others?

INSIGHTS

MAY 01　SATURDAY

CARD OF THE DAY:

▷ INTENTION

▷ REFLECTION

MAY 02　SUNDAY

CARD OF THE DAY:

▷ INTENTION

▷ REFLECTION

MAY 03　MONDAY

CARD OF THE DAY:

▷ INTENTION

▷ REFLECTION

MAY 04　TUESDAY

CARD OF THE DAY:

▷ INTENTION

▷ REFLECTION

MAY 05　WEDNESDAY

CARD OF THE DAY:

▷ INTENTION

▷ REFLECTION

MAY 06　THURSDAY | *Venus trine Pluto*

CARD OF THE DAY:

▷ INTENTION

▷ REFLECTION

MAY 07　FRIDAY

CARD OF THE DAY:

▷ INTENTION

▷ REFLECTION

MAY 08 SATURDAY · CARD OF THE DAY:

▷ INTENTION · ▷ REFLECTION

MAY 09 SUNDAY · CARD OF THE DAY:

▷ INTENTION · ▷ REFLECTION

MAY 10 MONDAY · CARD OF THE DAY:

▷ INTENTION · ▷ REFLECTION

MAY 11 TUESDAY | ○ *New Moon in Taurus* · CARD OF THE DAY:

▷ INTENTION · ▷ REFLECTION

MAY 12 WEDNESDAY · CARD OF THE DAY:

▷ INTENTION · ▷ REFLECTION

MAY 13 THURSDAY · CARD OF THE DAY:

▷ INTENTION · ▷ REFLECTION

MAY 14 FRIDAY · CARD OF THE DAY:

▷ INTENTION · ▷ REFLECTION

MAY 15   SATURDAY

CARD OF THE DAY:

▷ INTENTION

▷ REFLECTION

MAY 16   SUNDAY

CARD OF THE DAY:

▷ INTENTION

▷ REFLECTION

MAY 17   MONDAY

CARD OF THE DAY:

▷ INTENTION

▷ REFLECTION

MAY 18   TUESDAY

CARD OF THE DAY:

▷ INTENTION

▷ REFLECTION

MAY 19   WEDNESDAY

CARD OF THE DAY:

▷ INTENTION

▷ REFLECTION

MAY 20   THURSDAY

CARD OF THE DAY:

▷ INTENTION

▷ REFLECTION

MAY 21   FRIDAY | *Gemini season begins*

CARD OF THE DAY:

▷ INTENTION

▷ REFLECTION

MAY 22   SATURDAY   CARD OF THE DAY:

▷ INTENTION   ▷ REFLECTION

MAY 23   SUNDAY   CARD OF THE DAY:

▷ INTENTION   ▷ REFLECTION

MAY 24   MONDAY   CARD OF THE DAY:

▷ INTENTION   ▷ REFLECTION

MAY 25   TUESDAY   CARD OF THE DAY:

▷ INTENTION   ▷ REFLECTION

MAY 26   WEDNESDAY | ● *Full Moon in Sagittarius*   CARD OF THE DAY:

▷ INTENTION   ▷ REFLECTION

MAY 27   THURSDAY   CARD OF THE DAY:

▷ INTENTION   ▷ REFLECTION

MAY 28   FRIDAY   CARD OF THE DAY:

▷ INTENTION   ▷ REFLECTION

MAY 29 SATURDAY | *Mercury Retrograde begins* CARD OF THE DAY:

▷ INTENTION ▷ REFLECTION

MAY 30 SUNDAY CARD OF THE DAY:

▷ INTENTION ▷ REFLECTION

MAY 31 MONDAY CARD OF THE DAY:

▷ INTENTION ▷ REFLECTION

INSIGHTS

JUNE

THE EMPEROR

After the new beginnings and freedom of the Fool in May, the presence of the Emperor in June calls on you to buckle down and start implementing the structure and discipline you need to bring your newest ideas to fruition and create long-lasting success. Success is coming to you, but to receive this abundance you need to find a way to hold it in your energy sustainably. To do so, you must first create a solid foundation and structure designed to fully support this new level of success. Enough play — it's now time to work, and work you will! Start to get serious about what you want to manifest in your life and stay focused on your goals. Make structure and discipline your friends. Be systematic, strategic and highly organized in your approach, and trust me, you'll see progress this month.

 ### RITUAL: YOUR DAILY (DREAM) SCHEDULE

As you start the ritual, ask yourself, "What does a dream day look like for me?" How would you start your day? What would you do throughout the day? How would you feel by the end of the day? Write down your answers in your journal. Next, create a daily schedule, based on your dream day. Be intentional about where you choose to invest your time and energy. To close out the ritual, find the Emperor card in your favorite deck, and tune into his structured energy. What message of support and advice does he have for you as you embark on your daily (dream) schedule?

 ### CRYSTAL: TIGER'S EYE

A masculine stone known to strengthen will, mental clarity, and the good judgement needed to maintain focus unclouded from emotions.

ASTROLOGICAL INFLUENCES

June 2 | Venus into Cancer: Venus into Cancer inspires tenderness and self-protection. You may feel more sensitive during this time; try not to take things personally. It's a great time to tune into your emotional needs.

June 11 | Mars into Leo: Mars strides proudly into Leo. Indulge in ideas of grandeur, and go after what you truly want. Be bold, and enjoy the fiery passion this transit brings — but be careful not to engage in drama.

June 21 | Cancer season begins:
Nurturing, emotional, protected, romantic, loyal.

INSIGHTS

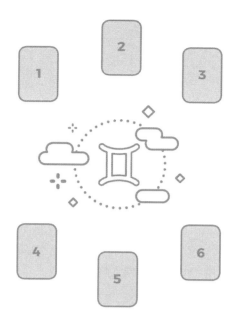

JUNE 10

NEW MOON IN GEMINI

A fresh New Moon in Gemini brings a sense of lightness. Set intentions around what you want to learn and teach, and how you can communicate for maximum effect.

1. How can I enhance my perceptions of the world around me?

2. What am I most curious about right now?

3. Where do I need to learn to verbalize my emotions?

4. What do I have to teach others?

5. What lessons can I learn from others?

6. How can I communicate with others in new and innovative ways?

INSIGHTS

JUNE 24

FULL MOON IN CAPRICORN

The Full Moon in Capricorn is a powerful time to reflect on your achievements. Where have you stood in integrity and built something you're proud of?

1. What am I most proud of achieving in the past six months?

2. What foundations do I most need to establish now to support future success?

3. What is a non-negotiable for me right now?

4. How can I help motivate others to work toward their own goals?

5. Which limiting beliefs are preventing me from setting bigger goals?

6. Where do I need to make more ethical choices?

INSIGHTS

JUN 01 TUESDAY   CARD OF THE DAY:

▷ INTENTION   ▷ REFLECTION

JUN 02 WEDNESDAY | *Venus into Cancer*   CARD OF THE DAY:

▷ INTENTION   ▷ REFLECTION

JUN 03 THURSDAY   CARD OF THE DAY:

▷ INTENTION   ▷ REFLECTION

JUN 04 FRIDAY   CARD OF THE DAY:

▷ INTENTION   ▷ REFLECTION

JUN 05 SATURDAY   CARD OF THE DAY:

▷ INTENTION   ▷ REFLECTION

JUN 06 SUNDAY   CARD OF THE DAY:

▷ INTENTION   ▷ REFLECTION

JUN 07 MONDAY   CARD OF THE DAY:

▷ INTENTION   ▷ REFLECTION

JUN 08 TUESDAY

CARD OF THE DAY:

▷ INTENTION

▷ REFLECTION

JUN 09 WEDNESDAY

CARD OF THE DAY:

▷ INTENTION

▷ REFLECTION

JUN 10 THURSDAY | ○ New Moon in Gemini

CARD OF THE DAY:

▷ INTENTION

▷ REFLECTION

JUN 11 FRIDAY | Mars into Leo

CARD OF THE DAY:

▷ INTENTION

▷ REFLECTION

JUN 12 SATURDAY

CARD OF THE DAY:

▷ INTENTION

▷ REFLECTION

JUN 13 SUNDAY

CARD OF THE DAY:

▷ INTENTION

▷ REFLECTION

JUN 14 MONDAY

CARD OF THE DAY:

▷ INTENTION

▷ REFLECTION

JUN 15 TUESDAY

CARD OF THE DAY:

▷ INTENTION

▷ REFLECTION

JUN 16 WEDNESDAY

CARD OF THE DAY:

▷ INTENTION

▷ REFLECTION

JUN 17 THURSDAY

CARD OF THE DAY:

▷ INTENTION

▷ REFLECTION

JUN 18 FRIDAY

CARD OF THE DAY:

▷ INTENTION

▷ REFLECTION

JUN 19 SATURDAY

CARD OF THE DAY:

▷ INTENTION

▷ REFLECTION

JUN 20 SUNDAY

CARD OF THE DAY:

▷ INTENTION

▷ REFLECTION

JUN 21 MONDAY | *Cancer season begins*

CARD OF THE DAY:

▷ INTENTION

▷ REFLECTION

JUN 22 TUESDAY

CARD OF THE DAY:

▷ INTENTION

▷ REFLECTION

JUN 23 WEDNESDAY

CARD OF THE DAY:

▷ INTENTION

▷ REFLECTION

JUN 24 THURSDAY | ● *Full Moon in Capricorn*

CARD OF THE DAY:

▷ INTENTION

▷ REFLECTION

JUN 25 FRIDAY

CARD OF THE DAY:

▷ INTENTION

▷ REFLECTION

JUN 26 SATURDAY

CARD OF THE DAY:

▷ INTENTION

▷ REFLECTION

JUN 27 SUNDAY

CARD OF THE DAY:

▷ INTENTION

▷ REFLECTION

JUN 28 MONDAY

CARD OF THE DAY:

▷ INTENTION

▷ REFLECTION

JUN 29 TUESDAY   CARD OF THE DAY:

▷ INTENTION   ▷ REFLECTION

JUN 30 WEDNESDAY   CARD OF THE DAY:

▷ INTENTION   ▷ REFLECTION

INSIGHTS

SUMMER SOLSTICE SPREAD

Summer Solstice (June 21, 3:32 am UTC in the Northern Hemisphere; December 21, 3:59 pm UTC in the Southern Hemisphere) is the time to shine and be seen! Be ready to step into the spotlight and express your true self to the world. Bask in the sunrays and allow yourself to be filled with light as you revel in a sense of accomplishment and fulfilment.

Now's the time! Watch as your projects crest towards completion and you are energized to take action on the new opportunities that arose during the Springtime. Use the following Tarot spread around the time of the Summer Solstice to connect with this sacred energy.

1. What new opportunities have emerged over the Spring?

2. How can I bring my current projects to fruition?

3. What is expanding in my life right now?

4. What blessings am I receiving?

5. What truly fulfills me?

6. How can I shine my light in the world?

INSIGHTS

INSIGHTS

SUMMER SOLSTICE INTENTIONS

Holding the energy and insight of your Summer Solstice Tarot Reading, set your intentions for the next three months:

JULY

THE HIEROPHANT

In July, the Hierophant invites you to search for teachers and guides who can support your spiritual growth and development. Choose teachers who have your best interest in mind, not their own self-serving goals. And be open to receive the wisdom of their established beliefs and traditions. This isn't about forging your own path, but rather, tapping into an existing mindset or belief system that can support your spiritual development. This month, you are also invited to establish or deepen your commitment to your spiritual practice. You may start a daily practice, or be called to something bigger such as taking a course, going on a retreat, or joining a spiritual group.

RITUAL: YOUR SPIRITUAL PRACTICE

Explore a new spiritual practice or discipline that you can implement in your life. Pick up a book or two about a religion or spiritual belief system you don't know much about. Or lose yourself in a new kind of yoga class. You might go on a peaceful retreat, like Vipassana (the 10-day silent meditation retreat). Or even make a commitment to daily meditation or chanting. Choose a practice that will deepen your connection with your spirit and that will teach you about an established belief system.

CRYSTAL: CELESTITE

Celestite is the "Teacher of the New Age" and is the perfect stone to support you along your path of spiritual awareness. A high-vibrational stone, Celestite will activate the Third Eye Chakra, allowing you to access your guides and all the knowledge they have to share with you.

ASTROLOGICAL INFLUENCES

July 1 | Mars opposition Saturn: Mars is irritated by roadblocks and limitations. Frustrations with rules, red tape, bosses and teachers may run high. Focus on long-term goals and practise mindfulness.

July 6 | Venus opposition Saturn: You may worry that you are undesirable or unlovable. Remember: you are your own worst enemy! Don't allow doubt or self-pity to creep in — switch your focus to self-love and gratitude.

July 22 | Leo season begins:
Pride, courage, warmth, audacity, generosity.

INSIGHTS

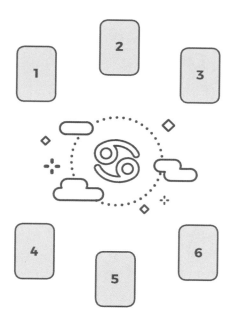

JULY 9
NEW MOON IN CANCER

If there were ever a time to make conscious choices about how you feel day-to-day, the New Moon in Cancer is the time. Dive into your emotional world and set empowering intentions around how you want to feel.

1. What new feelings are coming up for me right now?

2. Where do I need to empower myself to be more vulnerable in my relationships?

3. How might I benefit from setting boundaries?

4. How can I level-up my self-care practice?

5. What do I need to know about creating sacred space in my home?

6. What new approach can I take to support my emotional well-being?

INSIGHTS

JULY 23

FULL MOON IN AQUARIUS

The Full Moon in Aquarius invites you to explore the culmination of your efforts in the areas of personal freedom, community and progress towards your heart-centered goals.

1. How have my unique gifts had an impact on my community?

2. What do I need to let go of in order for my uniqueness to shine?

3. What do I need to know about my role in inspiring change for the greatest good?

4. How can I utilize all my platforms of communication to inspire positivity?

5. Why do I struggle to express certain feelings?

6. How has allowing myself to be more vulnerable impacted others positively?

INSIGHTS

On Instagram? Post a photo of your spread and your Tarot Planner with the hashtag **#biddytarotplanner** and we'll share with the Biddy Tarot community!

JUL 01 THURSDAY | *Mars opposition Saturn*

CARD OF THE DAY:

▷ INTENTION

▷ REFLECTION

JUL 02 FRIDAY

CARD OF THE DAY:

▷ INTENTION

▷ REFLECTION

JUL 03 SATURDAY

CARD OF THE DAY:

▷ INTENTION

▷ REFLECTION

JUL 04 SUNDAY

CARD OF THE DAY:

▷ INTENTION

▷ REFLECTION

JUL 05 MONDAY

CARD OF THE DAY:

▷ INTENTION

▷ REFLECTION

JUL 06 TUESDAY | *Venus opposition Saturn*

CARD OF THE DAY:

▷ INTENTION

▷ REFLECTION

JUL 07 WEDNESDAY

CARD OF THE DAY:

▷ INTENTION

▷ REFLECTION

JUL 08 THURSDAY

CARD OF THE DAY:

▷ INTENTION

▷ REFLECTION

JUL 09 FRIDAY | ○ New Moon in Cancer

CARD OF THE DAY:

▷ INTENTION

▷ REFLECTION

JUL 10 SATURDAY

CARD OF THE DAY:

▷ INTENTION

▷ REFLECTION

JUL 11 SUNDAY

CARD OF THE DAY:

▷ INTENTION

▷ REFLECTION

JUL 12 MONDAY

CARD OF THE DAY:

▷ INTENTION

▷ REFLECTION

JUL 13 TUESDAY

CARD OF THE DAY:

▷ INTENTION

▷ REFLECTION

JUL 14 WEDNESDAY

CARD OF THE DAY:

▷ INTENTION

▷ REFLECTION

JUL 15 THURSDAY
CARD OF THE DAY:

▷ INTENTION

▷ REFLECTION

JUL 16 FRIDAY
CARD OF THE DAY:

▷ INTENTION

▷ REFLECTION

JUL 17 SATURDAY
CARD OF THE DAY:

▷ INTENTION

▷ REFLECTION

JUL 18 SUNDAY
CARD OF THE DAY:

▷ INTENTION

▷ REFLECTION

JUL 19 MONDAY
CARD OF THE DAY:

▷ INTENTION

▷ REFLECTION

JUL 20 TUESDAY
CARD OF THE DAY:

▷ INTENTION

▷ REFLECTION

JUL 21 WEDNESDAY
CARD OF THE DAY:

▷ INTENTION

▷ REFLECTION

JUL 22 THURSDAY | *Leo season begins* CARD OF THE DAY:

▷ INTENTION ▷ REFLECTION

JUL 23 FRIDAY | ● *Full Moon in Aquarius* CARD OF THE DAY:

▷ INTENTION ▷ REFLECTION

JUL 24 SATURDAY CARD OF THE DAY:

▷ INTENTION ▷ REFLECTION

JUL 25 SUNDAY CARD OF THE DAY:

▷ INTENTION ▷ REFLECTION

JUL 26 MONDAY CARD OF THE DAY:

▷ INTENTION ▷ REFLECTION

JUL 27 TUESDAY CARD OF THE DAY:

▷ INTENTION ▷ REFLECTION

JUL 28 WEDNESDAY CARD OF THE DAY:

▷ INTENTION ▷ REFLECTION

JULY

JUL 29   THURSDAY   CARD OF THE DAY:

▷ INTENTION   ▷ REFLECTION

JUL 30   FRIDAY   CARD OF THE DAY:

▷ INTENTION   ▷ REFLECTION

JUL 31   SATURDAY   CARD OF THE DAY:

▷ INTENTION   ▷ REFLECTION

INSIGHTS

AUGUST

THE DEVIL

The appearance of the Devil in August brings conscious awareness to your attachments — negative habits, dependencies, behaviors, thought patterns, relationships, and addictions — that constrain you and hold you back from being the best version of yourself. In the search for immediate pleasure and gratification, you are putting your longer-term health and well-being at risk. This month, you are invited to shine the light of awareness on those attachments and the negative patterns that have been standing in your way for so long. Ask yourself: *What impact are they having on you? What do they serve? And how do they harm you?* Make a conscious decision about what you want to keep and what you want to release. You may not be completely free overnight, and it will take a tremendous amount of willpower to free yourself from their influence, but know that it *is* possible, and only you can make it happen.

 ### RITUAL: CUTTING THE CORDS

Find the Devil in your favorite Tarot deck and place it in front of you. Spend some time drawing in the energy of this card and listening to its messages for you. Then, in your journal, write down all of your unhealthy attachments and negative patterns. Close your eyes, and bring yourself into a state of reflective relaxation. Imagine you are holding a beautiful smoky quartz sword in your hands. Shift the sword to your left hand and begin making cutting motions over your body. With each strike, imagine you're clearing away any energy cords that may still be attached to you. Wave the sword, in your mind's eye, over the front and back of your body, over your head and under your feet. Continue until you feel complete, freeing yourself of the negativity, then gradually open your eyes.

 ### CRYSTAL: SMOKY QUARTZ

This powerful crystal helps you to let go of unhealthy attachments and old belief systems that are holding you back from achieving your highest potential. Once all of the old, stagnant energy is removed, new energy is able to fill all the open space with light.

ASTROLOGICAL INFLUENCES

August 9 | Venus opposition Neptune: Neptune casts a dreamy hue across romance and money, making it easy to overlook red flags. Decisions made now might come back to bite you. Focus on having fun with friends or family.

August 23 | Virgo season begins:
Practicality, order, creativity, analysis, service.

August 29 | Mercury into Libra: Rationality and negotiation are prominent themes. Reflect on disagreements, and try to see things from the other person's point of view. Listen objectively, but make your own choices.

INSIGHTS

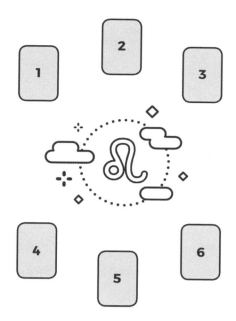

AUGUST 8

NEW MOON IN LEO

Your creations and passions are coming into focus with the New Moon in Leo. A time for setting courageous intentions about how you want to show up in the world.

1. What do I most want to create?

2. What can I do to express myself authentically in healthy, empowered ways?

3. What new aspects of myself am I discovering?

4. How can I be an effective and compassionate leader?

5. Where am I best-placed to lead by example?

6. Which areas of my life may require more courage in the next six months?

INSIGHTS

AUGUST 22

FULL MOON IN AQUARIUS

This second Full Moon in Aquarius amplifies the energy of the water-bearer, intensifying the energy of the previous Full Moon and bringing it into laser-sharp focus. Reflect on your notes from the July 23 Full Moon in Aquarius, and consider the impact your choices may be having on a much wider, even global, scale.

1. How can I utilize my unique gifts to contribute to global change?

2. Which beliefs may be having a detrimental affect on my community?

3. What global causes can I champion to have a greater impact on the world?

4. How can I help others to examine their beliefs about the global community?

5. Which forms of communication might I need to limit or release?

6. What can I do to empower others to become more vulnerable?

INSIGHTS

On Instagram? Post a photo of your spread and your Tarot Planner with the hashtag **#biddytarotplanner** and we'll share with the Biddy Tarot community!

86 | 2021 BIDDY TAROT PLANNER

AUG 01 SUNDAY   CARD OF THE DAY:

▷ INTENTION   ▷ REFLECTION

AUG 02 MONDAY   CARD OF THE DAY:

▷ INTENTION   ▷ REFLECTION

AUG 03 TUESDAY   CARD OF THE DAY:

▷ INTENTION   ▷ REFLECTION

AUG 04 WEDNESDAY   CARD OF THE DAY:

▷ INTENTION   ▷ REFLECTION

AUG 05 THURSDAY   CARD OF THE DAY:

▷ INTENTION   ▷ REFLECTION

AUG 06 FRIDAY   CARD OF THE DAY:

▷ INTENTION   ▷ REFLECTION

AUG 07 SATURDAY   CARD OF THE DAY:

▷ INTENTION   ▷ REFLECTION

AUG 08 SUNDAY | ○ *New Moon in Leo*   CARD OF THE DAY:

▷ INTENTION   ▷ REFLECTION

AUG 09 MONDAY | *Venus opposition Neptune*   CARD OF THE DAY:

▷ INTENTION   ▷ REFLECTION

AUG 10 TUESDAY   CARD OF THE DAY:

▷ INTENTION   ▷ REFLECTION

AUG 11 WEDNESDAY   CARD OF THE DAY:

▷ INTENTION   ▷ REFLECTION

AUG 12 THURSDAY   CARD OF THE DAY:

▷ INTENTION   ▷ REFLECTION

AUG 13 FRIDAY   CARD OF THE DAY:

▷ INTENTION   ▷ REFLECTION

AUG 14 SATURDAY   CARD OF THE DAY:

▷ INTENTION   ▷ REFLECTION

AUG 15   SUNDAY

CARD OF THE DAY:

▷ INTENTION   ▷ REFLECTION

AUG 16   MONDAY

CARD OF THE DAY:

▷ INTENTION   ▷ REFLECTION

AUG 17   TUESDAY

CARD OF THE DAY:

▷ INTENTION   ▷ REFLECTION

AUG 18   WEDNESDAY

CARD OF THE DAY:

▷ INTENTION   ▷ REFLECTION

AUG 19   THURSDAY

CARD OF THE DAY:

▷ INTENTION   ▷ REFLECTION

AUG 20   FRIDAY

CARD OF THE DAY:

▷ INTENTION   ▷ REFLECTION

AUG 21   SATURDAY

CARD OF THE DAY:

▷ INTENTION   ▷ REFLECTION

AUG 22   SUNDAY | ● *Full Moon in Aquarius*   CARD OF THE DAY:

▷ INTENTION   ▷ REFLECTION

AUG 23   MONDAY | *Virgo season begins*   CARD OF THE DAY:

▷ INTENTION   ▷ REFLECTION

AUG 24   TUESDAY   CARD OF THE DAY:

▷ INTENTION   ▷ REFLECTION

AUG 25   WEDNESDAY   CARD OF THE DAY:

▷ INTENTION   ▷ REFLECTION

AUG 26   THURSDAY   CARD OF THE DAY:

▷ INTENTION   ▷ REFLECTION

AUG 27   FRIDAY   CARD OF THE DAY:

▷ INTENTION   ▷ REFLECTION

AUG 28   SATURDAY   CARD OF THE DAY:

▷ INTENTION   ▷ REFLECTION

AUG 29 SUNDAY | *Mercury into Libra*

CARD OF THE DAY:

▷ INTENTION

▷ REFLECTION

AUG 30 MONDAY

CARD OF THE DAY:

▷ INTENTION

▷ REFLECTION

AUG 31 TUESDAY

CARD OF THE DAY:

▷ INTENTION

▷ REFLECTION

INSIGHTS

SEPTEMBER

THE EMPRESS

September brings an energy of abundance, creativity, fertility, beauty, and nourishment. You are surrounded by life's pleasures and luxuries and have everything you need to live a comfortable lifestyle. You are in a period of growth, in which all you have dreamed of is now coming to fruition. Take a moment to reflect on the bounty that surrounds you and offer gratitude for all you have created so you can continue to build on this energy and create even more abundance in your life. The time is ripe to bring your next big project into being. The Empress is your guide and encourages you to bring your abundant feminine energy to your work, to birth your new idea into the world. Get creative, play and have fun.

 ### RITUAL: BRING INTO FRUITION

This month is perfect for bringing your creative ideas into fruition, whether it's an art project, a new business, a new course or a new health regime. Choose one idea that really gets your creative juices flowing and lights you up from the inside out. Then, every day for the month of September (and longer if you feel called), do at least one thing to bring your idea into being. For an extra creative boost, meditate with the Empress card each day and invite her to bring her energy into your daily routine.

 ### CRYSTAL: MOONSTONE

Nurture yourself with the hopeful, soothing and inspirational energy of Moonstone. Unlock your inner goddess and allow the power of the Moonstone to support you. Just like the Moon, even if you can't see it, the energy of the Moonstone is there, pulling on your inner tides and setting your own natural rhythms back in balance.

⊘ ASTROLOGICAL INFLUENCES

September 5 | Mars trine Pluto: Pluto harnesses Mars' drive to succeed. Your efforts are likely to yield great results. Start a new project now while your determination is strong. Focus on making powerful choices for yourself.

September 23 | Libra season begins:
Balance, objectivity, fairness, aesthetics, charm.

September 28–October 16 | Mercury Retrograde in Libra: Utilize the Tarot Reader's Guide for Mercury Retrograde inside of your Toolkit www.biddytarot.com/2021-planner-bonus to help navigate through this time.

INSIGHTS

NEW MOON IN VIRGO

The New Moon in Virgo is an opportunity to get clear on how you want to be of service in the world and set your intentions around stepping into mastery. What will the best version of yourself be focused on during this lunar cycle?

1. How can I be of the highest service to my family, friends and partner?

2. Which area of my life would benefit most from evaluating my routine?

3. What change can I make to support my physical health and well-being?

4. What action can I take to bring a sense of order to my home?

5. What action can I take to process my thoughts more effectively?

6. What action can I take to gain further emotional clarity?

INSIGHTS

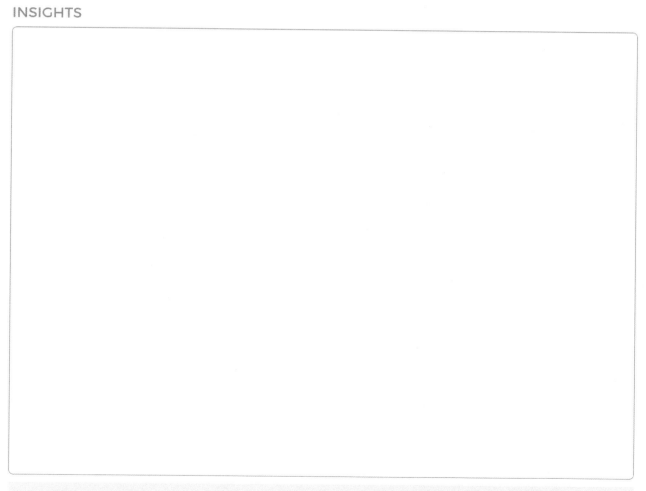

Don't forget to snap a pic of your reading and share on IG using the hashtag **#biddytarotplanner**.
We love seeing you using your Biddy Tarot Planner in action and can't wait to celebrate with you!

SEPTEMBER 20
FULL MOON IN PISCES

A dreamy Full Moon in Pisces can intensify your connection to spirit and your intuition. Celebrate the manifestation of your imaginings and release any wishful thinking that isn't serving you now.

1. Which areas of my life have benefited most from my intuition?

2. What do I need to release in order to connect with myself on a deeper level?

3. Where do I need to focus more gratitude in the next six months?

4. What limiting beliefs must I release to expand my creative projects?

5. What can I focus on to deepen my spiritual practice?

6. How might the arts inspire my own creative success moving forward?

INSIGHTS

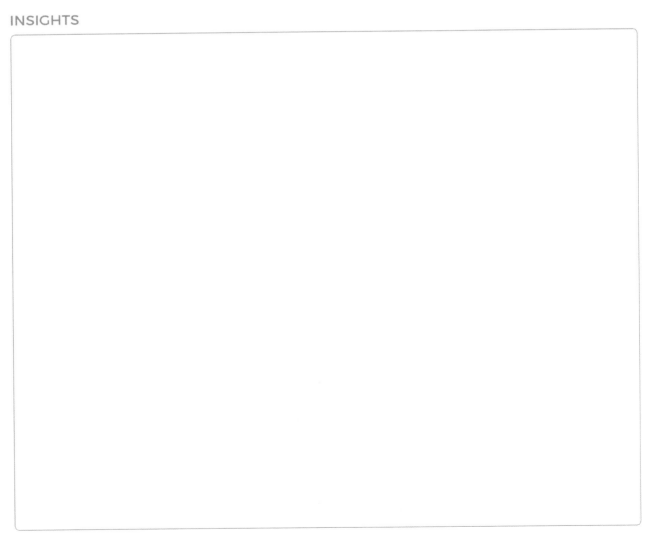

SEP 01   WEDNESDAY

CARD OF THE DAY:

▷ INTENTION

▷ REFLECTION

SEP 02   THURSDAY

CARD OF THE DAY:

▷ INTENTION

▷ REFLECTION

SEP 03   FRIDAY

CARD OF THE DAY:

▷ INTENTION

▷ REFLECTION

SEP 04   SATURDAY

CARD OF THE DAY:

▷ INTENTION

▷ REFLECTION

SEP 05   SUNDAY | *Mars trine Pluto*

CARD OF THE DAY:

▷ INTENTION

▷ REFLECTION

SEP 06   MONDAY | ○ *New Moon in Virgo*

CARD OF THE DAY:

▷ INTENTION

▷ REFLECTION

SEP 07   TUESDAY

CARD OF THE DAY:

▷ INTENTION

▷ REFLECTION

SEP 08 WEDNESDAY

CARD OF THE DAY:

▷ INTENTION

▷ REFLECTION

SEP 09 THURSDAY

CARD OF THE DAY:

▷ INTENTION

▷ REFLECTION

SEP 10 FRIDAY

CARD OF THE DAY:

▷ INTENTION

▷ REFLECTION

SEP 11 SATURDAY

CARD OF THE DAY:

▷ INTENTION

▷ REFLECTION

SEP 12 SUNDAY

CARD OF THE DAY:

▷ INTENTION

▷ REFLECTION

SEP 13 MONDAY

CARD OF THE DAY:

▷ INTENTION

▷ REFLECTION

SEP 14 TUESDAY

CARD OF THE DAY:

▷ INTENTION

▷ REFLECTION

SEP 15 WEDNESDAY   CARD OF THE DAY:

▷ INTENTION   ▷ REFLECTION

SEP 16 THURSDAY   CARD OF THE DAY:

▷ INTENTION   ▷ REFLECTION

SEP 17 FRIDAY   CARD OF THE DAY:

▷ INTENTION   ▷ REFLECTION

SEP 18 SATURDAY   CARD OF THE DAY:

▷ INTENTION   ▷ REFLECTION

SEP 19 SUNDAY   CARD OF THE DAY:

▷ INTENTION   ▷ REFLECTION

SEP 20 MONDAY | ● *Full Moon in Pisces*   CARD OF THE DAY:

▷ INTENTION   ▷ REFLECTION

SEP 21 TUESDAY   CARD OF THE DAY:

▷ INTENTION   ▷ REFLECTION

SEP 22 WEDNESDAY · CARD OF THE DAY:

▷ INTENTION · ▷ REFLECTION

SEP 23 THURSDAY | *Libra season begins* · CARD OF THE DAY:

▷ INTENTION · ▷ REFLECTION

SEP 24 FRIDAY · CARD OF THE DAY:

▷ INTENTION · ▷ REFLECTION

SEP 25 SATURDAY · CARD OF THE DAY:

▷ INTENTION · ▷ REFLECTION

SEP 26 SUNDAY · CARD OF THE DAY:

▷ INTENTION · ▷ REFLECTION

SEP 27 MONDAY · CARD OF THE DAY:

▷ INTENTION · ▷ REFLECTION

SEP 28 TUESDAY | *Mercury Retrograde begins* · CARD OF THE DAY:

▷ INTENTION · ▷ REFLECTION

SEP 29 WEDNESDAY

CARD OF THE DAY:

▷ INTENTION

▷ REFLECTION

SEP 30 THURSDAY

CARD OF THE DAY:

▷ INTENTION

▷ REFLECTION

INSIGHTS

FALL EQUINOX SPREAD

The Fall Equinox (September 22, 7:21 pm UTC in the Northern Hemisphere; March 20, 9:37 am in the Southern Hemisphere) is the time of harvest. After the abundance of the Summer, it's time to reap what you've sown, celebrate with deep appreciation, then bunker down for the Winter season. This is the perfect time for slowing down, expressing gratitude for what you've achieved, and gathering your resources for the Winter period.

Use the following Tarot spread around the Fall Equinox to connect with this sacred energy.

1. What have I achieved during the Summer period?

2. What is the bounty of my harvest?

3. What am I truly grateful for?

4. What resources are available to me now?

5. What resources do I need to gather?

6. What can I release and let go?

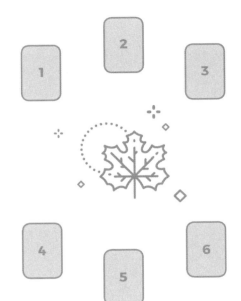

INSIGHTS

INSIGHTS

FALL EQUINOX INTENTIONS

Holding the energy and insight of your Fall Equinox Tarot Reading, set your intentions for the next three months:

OCTOBER

THE MOON

With the energy of the Moon, October is the month for the deep, intuitive work your soul is craving. Pull out your crystals, candles and Tarot cards, and pay attention to the subtle cues and symbols that are all around you. Messages are aplenty but you need to be tuned in to the collective energy to recognize and interpret them. Make spiritual self-care your priority and you'll reap the benefits. This is also the perfect time to tune into the moon cycles (see the ritual below) and make them a part of your life's flow. You may also feel a connection between the themes of October and March (High Priestess). Over this time, you have developed a deeper connection with your inner strength and have more confidence in your connection to your Higher Self. You believe in yourself and you're not afraid to be your fullest, intuitive self.

 ### RITUAL: HONORING THE MOON CYCLES

This month, you are invited to honor the Moon cycles and integrate them into your life's flow and natural rhythm. On the New Moon, set your intentions for growth and expansion for the next two weeks. And on the Full Moon, give thanks for what you have created, then release what no longer serves you. Amplify your commitment to this practice using the powerful New and Full Moon Rituals that are included in the bonus (and free!) Planner Toolkit at: www.biddytarot.com/2021-planner-bonus.

 ### CRYSTAL: SELENITE

Selenite is named after the Greek Goddess of the moon, Selene. Embodying the energy of the Goddess, Selenite will reflect back to you pure positive energy and clarity to guide you in maintaining connection with your Higher Self.

ASTROLOGICAL INFLUENCES

October 1 | Mercury square Pluto: You may find that your suspicions run high today, or you feel more negative or wary than usual. Be mindful when dealing with others that sometimes, it's best to hold your tongue.

October 13 | Venus sextile Saturn: Saturn brings a 'grown up' and stabilizing influence to love. New relationships feel more steady, and mature relationships find a new sense of realism. Ask a mature role model for relationship advice.

October 22 | Sagittarius season begins:
Adventure, optimism, philosophy, honesty, travel.

INSIGHTS

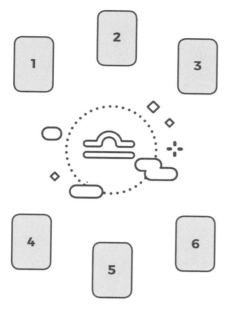

OCTOBER 6
NEW MOON IN LIBRA

A New Moon in Libra is a beautiful time to explore your personal values and the environment and relationships that support you in feeling balanced.

1. Where in my life would I benefit most from a deeper sense of harmony?

2. How might evaluating my personal style have a positive impact on my life?

3. How can I create more beauty in my environment?

4. Where would I benefit from a more peaceful approach?

5. How can I bond more strongly with others?

6. What is my true intention in my current or future relationship?

INSIGHTS

We love seeing you use your Biddy Tarot Planner! Completed this spread? Make sure you post a pic on Instagram and be sure to use the hashtag **#biddytarotplanner** so we can celebrate with you!

OCTOBER 20

FULL MOON IN ARIES

Honor your inner warrior with the Full Moon in Aries. Celebrate the ways you've grown into your strength, and release the fears that hold you back.

1. Where would I benefit most from being more fearless?

2. How can I release stress in a more constructive way?

3. Which battle is it time to release attachment to?

4. Where do I most need to be a little more selfish?

5. What do I need to release to be able to feel strong?

6. How can I be more compassionate toward others?

INSIGHTS

OCT 01 FRIDAY | *Mercury square Pluto* CARD OF THE DAY:

▷ INTENTION ▷ REFLECTION

OCT 02 SATURDAY CARD OF THE DAY:

▷ INTENTION ▷ REFLECTION

OCT 03 SUNDAY CARD OF THE DAY:

▷ INTENTION ▷ REFLECTION

OCT 04 MONDAY CARD OF THE DAY:

▷ INTENTION ▷ REFLECTION

OCT 05 TUESDAY CARD OF THE DAY:

▷ INTENTION ▷ REFLECTION

OCT 06 WEDNESDAY | ○ *New Moon in Libra* CARD OF THE DAY:

▷ INTENTION ▷ REFLECTION

OCT 07 THURSDAY CARD OF THE DAY:

▷ INTENTION ▷ REFLECTION

OCT 08 FRIDAY   CARD OF THE DAY:

▷ INTENTION   ▷ REFLECTION

OCT 09 SATURDAY   CARD OF THE DAY:

▷ INTENTION   ▷ REFLECTION

OCT 10 SUNDAY   CARD OF THE DAY:

▷ INTENTION   ▷ REFLECTION

OCT 11 MONDAY   CARD OF THE DAY:

▷ INTENTION   ▷ REFLECTION

OCT 12 TUESDAY   CARD OF THE DAY:

▷ INTENTION   ▷ REFLECTION

OCT 13 WEDNESDAY | *Venus sextile Saturn*   CARD OF THE DAY:

▷ INTENTION   ▷ REFLECTION

OCT 14 THURSDAY   CARD OF THE DAY:

▷ INTENTION   ▷ REFLECTION

OCT 15 FRIDAY

CARD OF THE DAY:

▷ INTENTION

▷ REFLECTION

OCT 16 SATURDAY | *Mercury Retrograde ends*

CARD OF THE DAY:

▷ INTENTION

▷ REFLECTION

OCT 17 SUNDAY

CARD OF THE DAY:

▷ INTENTION

▷ REFLECTION

OCT 18 MONDAY

CARD OF THE DAY:

▷ INTENTION

▷ REFLECTION

OCT 19 TUESDAY

CARD OF THE DAY:

▷ INTENTION

▷ REFLECTION

OCT 20 WEDNESDAY | ● *Full Moon in Aries*

CARD OF THE DAY:

▷ INTENTION

▷ REFLECTION

OCT 21 THURSDAY

CARD OF THE DAY:

▷ INTENTION

▷ REFLECTION

OCT 22 FRIDAY | *Sagittarius season begins*   CARD OF THE DAY:

▷ INTENTION   ▷ REFLECTION

OCT 23 SATURDAY   CARD OF THE DAY:

▷ INTENTION   ▷ REFLECTION

OCT 24 SUNDAY   CARD OF THE DAY:

▷ INTENTION   ▷ REFLECTION

OCT 25 MONDAY   CARD OF THE DAY:

▷ INTENTION   ▷ REFLECTION

OCT 26 TUESDAY   CARD OF THE DAY:

▷ INTENTION   ▷ REFLECTION

OCT 27 WEDNESDAY   CARD OF THE DAY:

▷ INTENTION   ▷ REFLECTION

OCT 28 THURSDAY   CARD OF THE DAY:

▷ INTENTION   ▷ REFLECTION

OCT 29 FRIDAY   CARD OF THE DAY:

▷ INTENTION   ▷ REFLECTION

OCT 30 SATURDAY   CARD OF THE DAY:

▷ INTENTION   ▷ REFLECTION

OCT 31 SUNDAY   CARD OF THE DAY:

▷ INTENTION   ▷ REFLECTION

INSIGHTS

NOVEMBER

THE TOWER

With the Tower card for November, expect the unexpected — massive change, upheaval, and destruction. Just when you think you're safe and comfortable, a Tower moment throws you for a loop. Your world may come crashing down before you, in ways you could never have imagined, as you realize that you've been building your life on unstable foundations — false assumptions, mistruths, illusions, blatant lies, and so on. Everything you thought to be true has turned on its head. This can be a very confusing and disorienting time, especially when your core belief systems are challenged. But you'll eventually come to see that they were built on a false understanding, and your new belief systems are more representative of reality. After a Tower experience, you grow stronger, wiser and more resilient as you develop a new perspective on life you did not even know existed. These moments are necessary for your spiritual growth and enlightenment. As you navigate these changing times, remember, truth and honesty will bring about a positive change.

 ### RITUAL: PERSONAL SURVIVAL GUIDE

Think of a time in your past when you experienced a Tower moment — when something so shocking and unexpected happened, you thought you'd never make it through. What happened? How did you pull through? What guidance do you have for yourself so that when you encounter shocks again in the future, you are well prepared? Write your insights down into your journal. Use your reflections to create your personal survival guide for the next time the Tower shows up in your life.

 ### CRYSTAL: OBSIDIAN

Obsidian is an excellent crystal to help anchor you in positivity and enlightenment while navigating through the turbulence and shake-ups that you may experience this month.

⊘ ASTROLOGICAL INFLUENCES

November 18 | Venus trine Uranus: You have permission to be 'weird' today! Embrace unusual social or romantic opportunities. Get creative while you're feeling upbeat — spontaneity can help facilitate growth.

November 22 | Scorpio season begins:
Transformation, intensity, ambition, control, reflection.

November 29 | Mars trine Neptune: Take a step back today. It's okay to bend and stretch your routine — watch a few movies, get artsy, or indulge in some well-deserved entertainment. Take advantage of unexpected inspiration.

INSIGHTS

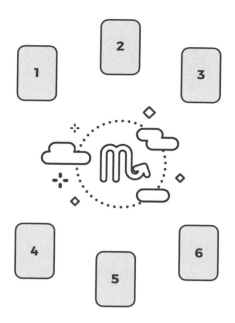

NOVEMBER 4

NEW MOON IN SCORPIO

The New Moon in Scorpio is the ideal time to make conscious decisions about your spiritual transformation. Use this time to set your intentions about who you're becoming.

1. Which area of my life might experience the deepest transformation in the next six months?

2. How can I healthily express my deepest desires?

3. Which elements of my shadow self need some attention and care?

4. How can I release the desire to control or manipulate outcomes?

5. Where am I not being truly honest with myself?

6. How can I foster a deeper connection with my spiritual truth?

INSIGHTS

NOVEMBER 19

FULL MOON IN TAURUS

Taurus Full Moon brings the focus to your physical resources and sense of peace. Luxuriate in sensual pleasures and release anything that feels like drama.

1. Which resources that I have gathered in the past six months will bring me the most joy?

2. What can I do to inspire more serenity in my life?

3. What do I need to do to feel more physically grounded?

4. How can I achieve a sense of absolute presence in my relationships?

5. What can I let go of now to make life feel easy?

6. How might my current or future relationship benefit from better understanding my sensuality?

INSIGHTS

NOV 01 MONDAY

CARD OF THE DAY:

▷ INTENTION

▷ REFLECTION

NOV 02 TUESDAY

CARD OF THE DAY:

▷ INTENTION

▷ REFLECTION

NOV 03 WEDNESDAY

CARD OF THE DAY:

▷ INTENTION

▷ REFLECTION

NOV 04 THURSDAY | ☼ *New Moon in Scorpio*

CARD OF THE DAY:

▷ INTENTION

▷ REFLECTION

NOV 05 FRIDAY

CARD OF THE DAY:

▷ INTENTION

▷ REFLECTION

NOV 06 SATURDAY

CARD OF THE DAY:

▷ INTENTION

▷ REFLECTION

NOV 07 SUNDAY

CARD OF THE DAY:

▷ INTENTION

▷ REFLECTION

NOV 08 MONDAY

CARD OF THE DAY:

▷ INTENTION

▷ REFLECTION

NOV 09 TUESDAY

CARD OF THE DAY:

▷ INTENTION

▷ REFLECTION

NOV 10 WEDNESDAY

CARD OF THE DAY:

▷ INTENTION

▷ REFLECTION

NOV 11 THURSDAY

CARD OF THE DAY:

▷ INTENTION

▷ REFLECTION

NOV 12 FRIDAY

CARD OF THE DAY:

▷ INTENTION

▷ REFLECTION

NOV 13 SATURDAY

CARD OF THE DAY:

▷ INTENTION

▷ REFLECTION

NOV 14 SUNDAY

CARD OF THE DAY:

▷ INTENTION

▷ REFLECTION

NOV 15 MONDAY

CARD OF THE DAY:

▷ INTENTION

▷ REFLECTION

NOV 16 TUESDAY

CARD OF THE DAY:

▷ INTENTION

▷ REFLECTION

NOV 17 WEDNESDAY

CARD OF THE DAY:

▷ INTENTION

▷ REFLECTION

NOV 18 THURSDAY | *Venus trine Uranus*

CARD OF THE DAY:

▷ INTENTION

▷ REFLECTION

NOV 19 FRIDAY | ● *Full Moon in Taurus*

CARD OF THE DAY:

▷ INTENTION

▷ REFLECTION

NOV 20 SATURDAY

CARD OF THE DAY:

▷ INTENTION

▷ REFLECTION

NOV 21 SUNDAY

CARD OF THE DAY:

▷ INTENTION

▷ REFLECTION

NOV 22 MONDAY | *Scorpio season begins*   CARD OF THE DAY:

▷ INTENTION   ▷ REFLECTION

NOV 23 TUESDAY   CARD OF THE DAY:

▷ INTENTION   ▷ REFLECTION

NOV 24 WEDNESDAY   CARD OF THE DAY:

▷ INTENTION   ▷ REFLECTION

NOV 25 THURSDAY   CARD OF THE DAY:

▷ INTENTION   ▷ REFLECTION

NOV 26 FRIDAY   CARD OF THE DAY:

▷ INTENTION   ▷ REFLECTION

NOV 27 SATURDAY   CARD OF THE DAY:

▷ INTENTION   ▷ REFLECTION

NOV 28 SUNDAY   CARD OF THE DAY:

▷ INTENTION   ▷ REFLECTION

NOV 29 MONDAY | *Mars trine Neptune*

CARD OF THE DAY:

▷ INTENTION

▷ REFLECTION

NOV 30 TUESDAY

CARD OF THE DAY:

▷ INTENTION

▷ REFLECTION

INSIGHTS

DECEMBER

THE LOVERS

What a beautiful way to end the year, with the Lovers card. The Lovers represent unity, harmony and balance, and this month, you bring together the parts of yourself and the world around you that are seemingly in opposition to one another. Use this energy of partnership and communion to create something that is 'whole', unified and harmonious. You have also learned to appreciate others' differences and to love others for their whole selves, not just the parts that please you. Finally, as this year comes to a close, you are surrounded by the people you love and who love you. Open your heart to give and receive love, and nurture your relationships with others through kindness and compassion.

RITUAL: OPENING THE HEART

To begin, take out the Lovers card from your Tarot deck and reflect on its energy. Then, find a quiet place, light a candle, and burn some rose or ylang ylang oil. Close your eyes and connect with your heart chakra and visualize a ball of pink light radiating from your heart center. Feel this light growing and growing as it fills your body, then radiates out into your aura, your room, your neighborhood, and eventually into the world and the Universe beyond. Take a moment to feel this deep, radiant love. Then, say this affirmation three times: *"I honor the love inside me and connect consciously with others."* When you're ready, open your eyes and journal about your experience.

CRYSTAL: ROSE QUARTZ

The stone of peace and unconditional love. It's effective in drawing in those loving relationships and deflecting negative energies. Rose Quartz will help you open your heart to love and beauty by healing unexpressed heartaches and transmuting internalized pains that no longer serve you.

ASTROLOGICAL INFLUENCES

December 22 | Capricorn season begins:
Persistence, realism, practicality, sensitivity, discipline.

December 25 | Venus conjunct Pluto: An 'all-in' attitude inspires animal magnetism today, making interaction with others effortless. Resist trying to manipulate others toward your point of view. Enjoy passionate, intense romance.

December 28 | Jupiter into Pisces: Jupiter into Pisces swells devotion and intuition. Motivations turn from outward ('What can I gain?'), to inward ('How can I help?'). This transit will help you write your most powerful gratitude list of 2021.

INSIGHTS

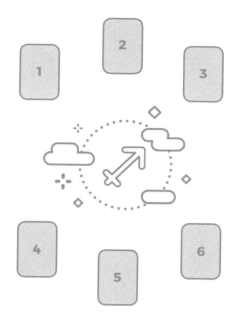

DECEMBER 3

NEW MOON IN SAGITTARIUS

The New Moon in Sagittarius encourages you to expand your awareness and perspective. Set intentions around adventures and experiences that will broaden your worldview.

1. Where do I need to focus on expanding my awareness?

2. What can I do to inspire a sense of adventure in my life?

3. What can I do to expand my friendship circles and connect with new people?

4. What is my ideal vision for the global community?

5. What lessons have I learned from travel in the past six months?

6. How can I utilize those lessons to inspire others?

INSIGHTS

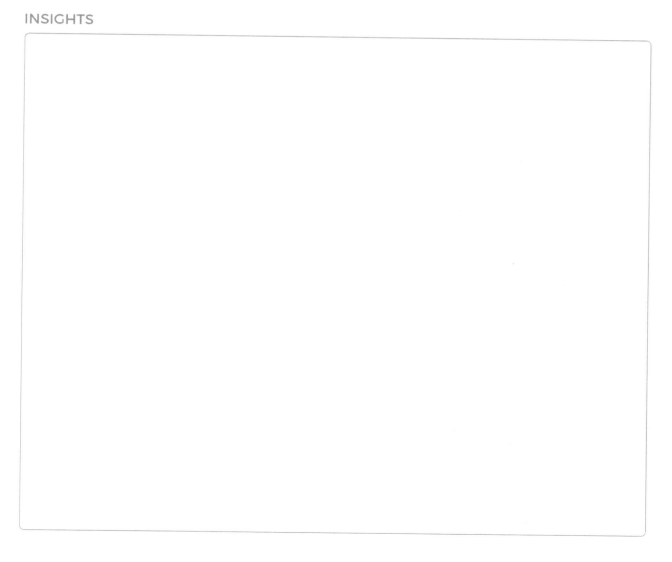

DECEMBER 18

FULL MOON IN GEMINI

The Full Moon in Gemini enhances your vitality and brings to light the ways you perceive the world. Release any feelings of boredom and explore your curiosities.

1. How have my perceptions of the world changed in the last six months?

2. What new information have I learned that I can now teach others?

3. How has verbalizing my emotions impacted my closest relationships this year?

4. What valuable lessons have I learned from others?

5. What valuable lessons have I been able to teach others?

6. How can I approach problems in a more logical and calculated way?

INSIGHTS

Don't forget to snap a pic of your reading and share on IG using the hashtag #biddytarotplanner.
We love seeing you using your Biddy Tarot Planner in action and can't wait to celebrate with you!

120 | 2021 BIDDY TAROT PLANNER

DEC 01 WEDNESDAY

CARD OF THE DAY:

▷ INTENTION

▷ REFLECTION

DEC 02 THURSDAY

CARD OF THE DAY:

▷ INTENTION

▷ REFLECTION

DEC 03 FRIDAY

CARD OF THE DAY:

▷ INTENTION

▷ REFLECTION

DEC 04 SATURDAY | ○ *New Moon in Sagittarius*

CARD OF THE DAY:

▷ INTENTION

▷ REFLECTION

DEC 05 SUNDAY

CARD OF THE DAY:

▷ INTENTION

▷ REFLECTION

DEC 06 MONDAY

CARD OF THE DAY:

▷ INTENTION

▷ REFLECTION

DEC 07 TUESDAY

CARD OF THE DAY:

▷ INTENTION

▷ REFLECTION

DEC 08 WEDNESDAY

CARD OF THE DAY:

▷ INTENTION

▷ REFLECTION

DEC 09 THURSDAY

CARD OF THE DAY:

▷ INTENTION

▷ REFLECTION

DEC 10 FRIDAY

CARD OF THE DAY:

▷ INTENTION

▷ REFLECTION

DEC 11 SATURDAY

CARD OF THE DAY:

▷ INTENTION

▷ REFLECTION

DEC 12 SUNDAY

CARD OF THE DAY:

▷ INTENTION

▷ REFLECTION

DEC 13 MONDAY

CARD OF THE DAY:

▷ INTENTION

▷ REFLECTION

DEC 14 TUESDAY

CARD OF THE DAY:

▷ INTENTION

▷ REFLECTION

DEC 15 WEDNESDAY   CARD OF THE DAY:

▷ INTENTION   ▷ REFLECTION

DEC 16 THURSDAY   CARD OF THE DAY:

▷ INTENTION   ▷ REFLECTION

DEC 17 FRIDAY   CARD OF THE DAY:

▷ INTENTION   ▷ REFLECTION

DEC 18 SATURDAY | ● *Full Moon in Gemini*   CARD OF THE DAY:

▷ INTENTION   ▷ REFLECTION

DEC 19 SUNDAY   CARD OF THE DAY:

▷ INTENTION   ▷ REFLECTION

DEC 20 MONDAY   CARD OF THE DAY:

▷ INTENTION   ▷ REFLECTION

DEC 21 TUESDAY   CARD OF THE DAY:

▷ INTENTION   ▷ REFLECTION

DEC 22 WEDNESDAY | *Capricorn season begins*   CARD OF THE DAY:

▷ INTENTION   ▷ REFLECTION

DEC 23 THURSDAY   CARD OF THE DAY:

▷ INTENTION   ▷ REFLECTION

DEC 24 FRIDAY   CARD OF THE DAY:

▷ INTENTION   ▷ REFLECTION

DEC 25 SATURDAY | *Venus conjunct Pluto*   CARD OF THE DAY:

▷ INTENTION   ▷ REFLECTION

DEC 26 SUNDAY   CARD OF THE DAY:

▷ INTENTION   ▷ REFLECTION

DEC 27 MONDAY   CARD OF THE DAY:

▷ INTENTION   ▷ REFLECTION

DEC 28 TUESDAY | *Jupiter into Pisces*   CARD OF THE DAY:

▷ INTENTION   ▷ REFLECTION

DEC 29   WEDNESDAY

CARD OF THE DAY:

▷ INTENTION

▷ REFLECTION

DEC 30   THURSDAY

CARD OF THE DAY:

▷ INTENTION

▷ REFLECTION

DEC 31   FRIDAY

CARD OF THE DAY:

▷ INTENTION

▷ REFLECTION

INSIGHTS

WINTER SOLSTICE SPREAD

Winter Solstice (December 21 3:58 pm UTC in the Northern Hemisphere; June 21 4:31 am UTC in the Southern Hemisphere), is the perfect time to go within, to step into the darkness and hibernate, and to reflect on your shadow self (the part of you that you try to deny or hide from others). Through this self-reflection, you'll emerge once again into the light as your most powerful self.

Use the following Tarot spread during the Winter Solstice to connect with this sacred energy.

1. What is the essence of my inner shadow self?

2. What can I learn from my shadow self?

3. How can I bring my shadow self into the light?

4. What lights me up from within?

5. What new seeds am I planting?

6. What do I need to release in order to create space for growth?

INSIGHTS

INSIGHTS

WINTER SOLSTICE INTENTIONS

Holding the energy and insight of your Winter Solstice Tarot Reading, set your intentions for the next three months:

2021 REFLECTION

As we come to the end of 2021, take some time to reflect on the past 12 months and prepare yourself for the year to come. Go back to the New Year's Tarot Spread you completed in January and reflect on what has emerged over the course of the year.

Then, go through the questions below and for each one, journal your intuitive thoughts first, then if you feel called to do so, draw a Tarot card to help you go deeper.

1. What were my biggest achievements for 2021?

2. What were my biggest challenges for 2021?

3. How have I developed as a person?

4. What did I learn in 2021?

5. How would I describe 2021 in just 3 words?

6. What is now complete?

7. What continues into 2022?

8. What new seeds and opportunities are being planted?

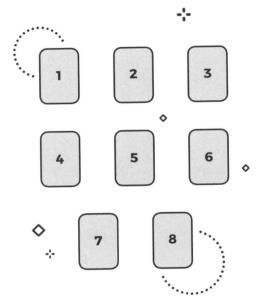

1. WHAT WERE MY BIGGEST ACHIEVEMENTS FOR 2021?

On Instagram? Post a photo of your spread and your Tarot Planner with the hashtag **#biddytarotplanner** and we'll share with the Biddy Tarot community!

2. WHAT WERE MY BIGGEST CHALLENGES FOR 2021?

3. HOW HAVE I DEVELOPED AS A PERSON?

4. WHAT DID I LEARN IN 2021?

5. HOW WOULD I DESCRIBE 2021 IN JUST 3 WORDS?

6. WHAT IS NOW COMPLETE?

7. WHAT CONTINUES INTO 2022?

8. WHAT NEW SEEDS AND OPPORTUNITIES ARE BEING PLANTED?

THE BIDDY TAROT PRODUCT SUITE

Access these Biddy Tarot products to elevate YOUR highest learning potential. Learn more about these resources — and our full range of Tarot courses and programs — to help you on your journey at www.biddytarot.com/shop.

THE ULTIMATE GUIDE TO TAROT CARD MEANINGS
Fresh, Modern, Practical Guide To The Meanings Of Every Tarot Card

The *Ultimate Guide to Tarot Card Meanings* has everything you need to read the Tarot cards as simply as reading a magazine. Just imagine — all the Tarot card meanings you could ever want, right at your fingertips in this comprehensive, 400+ page reference guide. You'll never need to buy another book on Tarot card meanings again!

Available for purchase at www.biddytarot.com/guide.

INTUITIVE TAROT: 31 DAYS TO LEARN TO READ TAROT CARDS AND DEVELOP YOUR INTUITION
Trust Your Intuition, Access Your Inner Power, And Bring The Divine Into Your Everyday Life

With *Intuitive Tarot*, you can learn to access your intuition and confidently read the cards without a reference guide. Imagine the thrill of looking at a card (or even a full Tarot spread) and instantly understanding the message it has for you. Through 31 daily lessons and activities, you'll learn to quickly and accurately interpret the cards, and unlock the secrets to an insightful reading. It's already inside you — you just need to trust it.

Available for purchase at www.biddytarot.com/tarot-guides/intuitive-tarot.

TAROT 101
A Step-By-Step Beginner Video Series and Workbook for Tarot Lovers Everywhere

Do you want to learn to connect with the Tarot and trust your intuition? *Tarot 101* is the ultimate course for Tarot beginners eager to harness the powerful messages of the cards. The guided program features in-depth lessons, including steps on how to do readings with clarity and tell an accurate and insightful story with the cards. Are you ready to start your Tarot journey? Sign up for the *Tarot 101* program today!

Available for purchase at www.biddytarot.com/tarot-101-course.

MASTER THE TAROT CARD MEANINGS PROGRAM

Stop Memorizing the Cards and Start Listening to Your Intuition

The *Master the Tarot Card Meanings* program will help you learn to read Tarot from your heart, not a book. Each lesson empowers you to build a unique personal connection with the Tarot, using simple yet powerful techniques for interpreting the cards. In just seven courses, you'll unlock the secrets of the Major and Minor Arcana, court cards, and reversed readings using numerology, symbolism, and so much more. By the end of the program, you'll have the power to intuitively access the meaning behind any spread!

Available for purchase at www.biddytarot.com/mtcm.

THE BIDDY TAROT COMMUNITY

Join a global, online community of 2000+ Tarot lovers and develop your Tarot reading skills

The Biddy Tarot Community is the only online community of its kind. Connect with 2,000+ Tarot lovers all over the world and get resources to help you learn and grow in your practice. Members get access to tons of Tarot resources, exclusive classes, the free tarot reading platform to practice readings, and a unique TarotPath to help you level up on your Tarot journey.

Join the Biddy Tarot Community at www.biddytarot.com/community.